Mental Health

ISSUES FOR THE NINETIES

Volume 21

Editor

Craig Donnellan

Independence
Educational Publishers

First published by Independence
PO Box 295
Cambridge CB1 3XP

© Craig Donnellan 1995

British Library Cataloguing in Publication Data
Mental Health – (Issues for the Nineties Series)
I. Donnellan, Craig II. Series
362.2

ISBN 1 872995 62 4

Printed in Great Britain
at Leicester Printers Ltd
Leicester

Cover
The cartoon on the front cover is by
the artist, Ken Pyne.

Typeset by
Martyn Lusher Artwork
Cambridge

CONTENTS

Introduction

Mental Health is the twenty-first volume in the series: **Issues For The Nineties**. The aim of this series is to offer up-to-date information about important issues in our world.

Mental Health examines the nature of mental illness in various groups in the community and the debate about community care. The information comes from a wide variety of sources and includes:

Government reports and statistics
Newspaper reports and features
Magazine articles and surveys
Literature from lobby groups
and charitable organisations.

It is hoped that, as you read about the many aspects of the issues explored in this book, you will critically evaluate the information presented. It is important that you decide whether you are being presented with facts or opinions. Does the writer give a biased or an unbiased report? If an opinion is being expressed, do you agree with the writer?

Mental Health offers a useful starting point for those who need convenient access to information about the many issues involved. However, it is only a starting point. At the back of the book is a list of organisations which you may want to contact for further information.

*****

Emotional and mental health problems in the young

The facts

Two million children and young people suffer from mental distress. Problems tend to become more apparent in older children. Young adolescents (aged 14–15) are three times more likely to have emotional and conduct disorders than children aged 10–11 years.

It is often difficult to correctly identify the problems. Studies show that 23% of children attending GP surgeries (2 million) have some form of psychological or emotional problem, but only 2% are identified by GPs (173,000). Even in paediatric outpatients clinics, only 1 in 3 cases is identified.

Most problems are relatively mild and temporary, perhaps brought on by particular life events such as a change of school. However, 250,000 children under the age of 16 in the UK (2%) are affected by problems which need specialist help. Approximately 10,000 suffer from psychotic illness (which affects the ability to distinguish between reality and imagination), usually following the onset of puberty.

Special services for children and young people in distress are inadequate and children and young people are increasingly having to be treated in adult units. The Department of Health has stated that, between 1985 and 1990, the number of NHS psychiatric admissions of those aged between 10 and 14 rose from 145 to 176 per 100,000. Admissions of under-10s rose by 42% and of 15 to 19-year-olds by 21%. By comparison, adult admissions fell 9%, to 2,692 per 100,000.

The above statistics are quoted from *Mental Illness: The Fundamental Facts*, published by the Mental Health Foundation.

What sort of problems do children and young people experience?

Common psychological and emotional problems include eating disorders such as anorexia or bulimia, sleep difficulties, aggression, subdued behaviour and failure to thrive. Small children may stop talking after seeing language as a weapon or a source of unhappiness at home, or because they don't get a proper response from their parents when they do talk. Older children may stop learning at school or be unable to make friends and find themselves isolated and lonely.

Depression: Just like adults, children and young people get depressed, but they are more likely to talk about feeling miserable, fed-up or bored. Sometimes they may say that they wish they were dead. Young adolescents often feel miserable, but when they get depressed they may become withdrawn and stay in their room. Depression may affect their performance at school. Alternatively, they may become angry or cry, or say that they are no good. They may start to misuse alcohol or drugs.

Anxiety: Anxiety in childhood and adolescence can be general or be focused upon a particular thing and become a fear. In both cases the anxiety or fear may be justifiable or illogical. Small children may cling excessively when anxious, insecure, miserable or preoccupied. Older children may appear wary or tense, have problems with sleeping, flinch very easily when startled and be constantly asking for reassurance.

School Phobia: Some children develop a powerful fear of attending

school and find themselves unable to leave home and go to school. This often becomes an issue after a child has been off school with an illness.

Obsessions: These are anxious, repetitive thoughts that crowd unwelcomed into the mind and are difficult to get rid of. Often they give rise to compulsive rituals such as counting, hand-washing or cleaning which are intended to ward off such thoughts or deal with the anxieties that they produce. These obsessional rituals are unpleasant and severe, much more distressing than the simple rituals that children put into their games.

Why do they have these problems?

Problems can arise in the family, school or through friends and activities away from home. Young children are more likely to become anxious for reasons to do with their family. With older children and teenagers, factors outside the home, such as problems with authorities, become increasingly important.

The risk of childhood mental health problems increases in families under stress, perhaps because parents are unemployed, living alone or homeless, where a parent suffers from mental illness or when child abuse occurs. Many children who run away from home do so because of physical or sexual abuse and this may lead to mental distress. Problems within the family include rows between parents, parental illness, parents using excessive threats to control their children and parents who overexpose children to adult worries (sex, money, unemployment). Conversely, excessive secrecy and failure to communicate openly with children can also cause distress.

Areas of difficulty at school include trouble with other children (bullying, rejection and teasing), trouble with work (grades and exam results) and trouble with teachers.

Young people may also get anxious concerning physical appearance, girl- and boyfriends or trouble with authorities such as the police.

Where can parents/carers get help?

It is important that parents and carers who are worried about the mental health of children or young people seek advice early, before problems become established. Firstly, they should approach their family doctor, who will help directly or refer them to a specialist if necessary. Health visitors and schools offer advice on how to care for children whose behaviour is difficult to manage, and educational psychologists can offer professional help on school-related problems. The local specialist Child and Family Service, sometimes known as Child Guidance or The Child and Adolescent Centre, can also be contacted through the local health authority.

The Mental Health Foundation supports research and innovative community projects working with children and young people with mental health problems.

For further information please contact:
Information Office
The Mental Health Foundation
37 Mortimer Street
London W1N 8JU
Tel: 0171-580 0145

Mental illness among children up by 25% in 5 years

The number of children and teenagers suffering from serious mental illnesses and admitted to psychiatric hospitals has increased by almost 25 per cent over five years, from 7,000 in 1986 to a record 8,800 in 1991.

Explanations may be that many more youngsters are being treated in inappropriate adult facilities, as they were in Victorian times, or that there has been a real increase in emotional and behavioural problems among young people consistent with the dramatic rise in the divorce rate and family break-ups.

The latest figures from the Department of Health show the most striking increase is among children under the age of 10: the number in this age group admitted to hospital has almost doubled from 707 to 1,400.

The next largest rise was among children aged between 10 and 14, whose numbers rose by almost 50 per cent from 1,077 to 1,600. The number of 15 to 19-year-olds admitted rose by 10 per cent, from 5,272 to 5,800. The latest increase continues a pattern of rises since 1985 and contrasts with a decrease which occurred from 7,717 in 1979 to 7,337 in 1985.

Many child psychiatrists and children's rights campaigners have anecdotal evidence that a growing number of teenagers are being 'dumped' in adult wards, a practice condemned by most doctors.

Today, researchers from South West Thames Regional Health Authority who have conducted a national review of mental health services for children and adolescents will present their preliminary findings to the Department of Health. The results are believed to show a breakdown in the co-ordinated programmes of care involving health authorities, the education service and social services departments. Local authority departments have been hit by funding cuts.

Young Minds, the National Association for Child and Family Mental Health, has called for a national plan for children's and adolescent mental health, and warns: 'The effects of all these closures and reductions are very serious indeed. The scope for early intervention, particularly with vulnerable families, becomes increasingly limited.'

Surviving adolescence

From the Royal College of Psychiatrists

Introduction

The teenage years can be an emotional assault course for all concerned. Parents and their teenage offspring may seem to be at each other's throats. The special name for this stormy time is adolescence. However, recent studies have shown that most teenagers actually like their parents and feel that they get on well with them. So why do so many people find adolescence so difficult? It's a time of rapid physical development and deep emotional changes. These can be exciting, but also confusing and uncomfortable for child and parent alike. In this article you will find information about these changes, the upheavals they can cause, the special problems that arise and ways in which they can be managed.

The changes of adolescence

The rapid changes of adolescence start gradually, from around eleven years for girls, thirteen for boys. The hormone changes responsible actually begin some years earlier and may produce periods of moodiness and restlessness. Girls start these changes before boys and will, for the first three or four years, appear to be maturing much faster. After this, boys catch up. By the age of 17, they'll be young men and women who may be as big as their parents and capable of having children themselves. This is all complicated by the fact that a daughter's ability to conceive may emerge at the time her mother is losing hers – the menopause. The good times and opportunities that adolescent children have may well make their parents feel very middle-aged and even envious.

It is not surprising that, with the speed of these changes, some adolescents become very concerned about their appearance. They may need a lot of reassurance, especially if they are not growing or maturing as quickly as their friends. They and their parents may worry less if they are aware that there's a lot of difference in the ages at which rapid growth occurs, at which girls have their first period or at which boys' voices break. All this growth and development uses a lot of energy, and this may be why teenagers often seem to need so much sleep. Their getting up late may be irritating, but it may well not be just laziness.

As well as growing taller, starting to shave or having periods, people of this age start to think and feel differently. They start to make close relationships outside the family, with friends of their own age. Relationships within the family also change. Parents become less all-important in their children's eyes as life outside the family develops.

Real disagreements emerge for the first time as young people develop views of their own that are often not shared by their parents. As everybody knows, adolescents spend a lot of time in each other's company, or on the telephone to each other. Although this can be irritating to parents, it is an important way of gaining a sense of identity that is distinct from that of the family. These friendships are part of learning how to get on with other people. Clothes and appearance become very important, both as a way of expressing solidarity with friends, and as a way of declaring a growing independence from the family.

Parents often feel rejected, and in a sense they are. But this apparent rejection is necessary for young people to become adults with their own identity. Rows and arguments may be frequent, yet adolescents will usually hold their parents in high regard. The rejections and conflicts are often not to do with parents' personalities but simply with the fact that they are parents, from whom their children must become increasingly independent if they are to have their own life.

Striving to become more independent, young people want to try out new things, but often recognise that they have little experience to fall back on when under stress. This may produce rapid changes in self-confidence and behaviour – appearing to be very grown up one minute, very young the next. Being upset or lacking confidence can make them feel childish, and so is often expressed in sulky behaviour rather than open distress. Parents have to be pretty flexible to deal with all this, and may feel under considerable strain themselves.

Taking risks

Adolescence is the time when people first start to learn about the world in earnest and to find their place in it. This involves trying out new experiences, some of which may be risky or even dangerous. People of this age crave excitement in a way that most adults find difficult to understand – and exciting activities may be dangerous ones. Fortunately most people manage to find their excitement in music, sport, or other activities that involve a lot of energy but little real physical risk.

Whatever experimentation does take place – with drink or drugs or smoking – is usually in the company of others. Those who do so alone are in much greater danger. Warnings from older adolescents may well have more effect than those from adults.

Common problems

1   Emotional Problems

Research has shown that at some time 4 out of 10 adolescents have felt so miserable that they have cried and have wanted to get away from everyone and everything. In the course of their adolescence, more than 1 in 5 think so little of themselves that life does not seem worth living. These common feelings can produce a state of depression that may not be obvious to other people. Over-eating, excessive sleepiness and a persistent overconcern with appearance may also be signs of emotional distress. More obviously, phobias and panic attacks may appear. Recent research suggests that emotional disorders are often not recognised, even by family and friends.

2   Sexual problems

The dramatic physical changes of adolescence can be very worrying to some teenagers, especially to those who are shy and who don't like to ask questions. At the other end of the scale, concern may show up in excessive bragging about sexual ability and experiences. More than half will have had their first experience of penetrative sex before the age of 16 and so the fear and risk of pregnancy

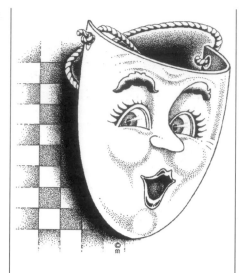

are an important part of adolescent life. Also it is not lawful for boys to have sex with girls who are less than 16. Those who begin penetrative sex early are at greater risk of early pregnancy and health problems. The new risks of HIV infection and AIDS cause great concern to many. There may also be doubts about whether an adolescent is gay or straight by some young people and their parents.

Sensitive support, clear guidance and accurate information about these different aspects of sex are greatly appreciated – from parents, schools, family doctors, and sometimes family planning clinics.

Most adolescents are quite careful in their choice of partners. Promiscuity and repeated, risky, unprotected intercourse are often signs of underlying emotional problems. They may also be the signs of a risk-taking lifestyle – adolescents who take risks in one way tend to take risks all-round.

3   Behaviour problems

Teenagers and their parents complain about each other's behaviour. Parents often feel they have lost any sort of control or influence over their child. At the same time as wanting their parents to be clear, wanting some structure and boundaries, adolescents resent parental restrictions on their growing freedom and ability to decide for themselves. Disagreements are common, part of the young person's struggle to forge a separate identity. This is all normal, but may get to the point where parents have really lost control, not knowing where their children are,

what they are up to, or what is happening to them. Experience suggests that children are at greater risk of getting into trouble if their parents don't know where they are, so it is important that they let their parents know where they are going and that parents ask.

4   School problems

Refusal to go to school is commonly due to difficulties in separating from parents, and may have happened before in primary school. Such children commonly suffer physical symptoms such as headache or stomach-ache.

Those who go to school, but then play truant, are usually unhappy at home and frustrated at school, so spend their days with others who feel the same way.

Emotional problems will often affect school work – worry about oneself, or about what is going on at home, makes it difficult to concentrate.

Pressure to do well and to pass exams may come from parents or teachers, but adolescents usually want to do well and will push themselves.

Excessive nagging can be counter-productive. Exams are important, but they should not be allowed to dominate life or to cause unhappiness.

5   Trouble with the law

Most young people do not break the law, and those that do are usually boys. When they do, it usually only happens once. Repeated offending may reflect a family culture, but may also result from unhappiness or distress – so it is always worth asking about these feelings when an adolescent is repeatedly getting into trouble.

6   Eating problems

A common cause of unhappiness is being fat, which may cause a vicious circle to develop. Overweight adolescents who are criticised or made fun of, maybe at home, maybe at school, or both, become depressed and grow to dislike themselves. This leads to inactivity and comfort eating, which worsens the weight problem. Dieting can actually aggravate the situation – it is more important to ensure that they feel happy with themselves, fat or thin.

Many adolescents diet, particularly girls, but fortunately very few will develop serious eating disorders, anorexia or bulimia. However, these are more likely to occur in those who take up serious dieting, think very little of themselves, are under stress and who have been overweight as a child. (see The Royal College of Psychiatrists' *Help is at Hand* leaflet on anorexia and bulimia).

7 *Drugs, solvents and alcohol*
Most teenagers never use drugs or inhale solvents, and most that do never get beyond experimenting with them. Despite the publicity about other drugs, alcohol is the most common drug which causes problems for adolescents. The possibility of any form of drug use should be considered when parents notice serious, sudden changes in behaviour.

8 *Abuse*
Finally, physical, emotional and sexual abuse may occur in adolescence and may cause many of the problems mentioned above. Families with these problems need expert advice and should seek help. The list of organisations at the back of this book may be able to point you in the right direction.

Less common problems
Much less often, changes in behaviour and mood can mark the beginning of more serious psychiatric disorders.

Although uncommon, manic depression and schizophrenia may emerge for the first time during adolescent years. Extreme withdrawal may indicate schizophrenia, though there are usually other explanations for such behaviour. Parents who are concerned about these possibilities should seek further information from their family doctor.

How to cope
Adolescence can be a time when the process of growing up can help people to make positive changes and to put the problems of the past behind them. It is not just a difficult stage, although it can feel very much like it at times.

The anxiety experienced by parents is more than matched by the periods of uncertainty, turmoil and unhappiness experienced by the

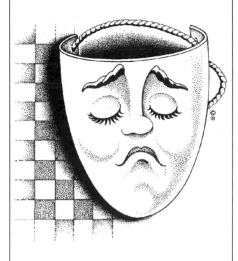

adolescent. In spite of this, most don't develop serious problems, although difficult times come and go.

Most difficulties in adolescence are not serious or long-term. This may be cold comfort to those who are struggling to get through it. Parents may even start to feel that they have failed. However, whatever may be said in the heat of the moment, parents still play a crucial part in their children's lives.

One of their jobs is to provide a secure base for their offspring to come back to. The first way to ensure this is for parents to agree between themselves and support each other. One parent allying her/himself with a child against the other parent is a recipe for disaster.

The next requirement is – rules. However fast people are growing up, parents are the children's providers and it is reasonable that they should decide what the ground rules are. Whilst adolescents may protest, sensible rules can be the basis for security and agreement. They must be clear, so everybody knows where they stand, and must be applied consistently.

Rules should be reasonable and become less restrictive as older children become more responsible. Parents need to sort out what is important and what isn't, so that there aren't rules for everything. While some issues will not be negotiable, there should be room for bargaining on others. Sanctions such as grounding or loss of pocket money will work better if they are established in advance; these should never be

threatened if they are not going to be carried out.

Another task for adults is to be a source of advice, sympathy and comfort. This will only happen if adolescents know that their parents will not automatically jump down their throats with a judgement, a criticism or routine advice. Listening is what's needed first.

Lastly, parents shouldn't expect their children to be grateful – they probably won't be until they have children of their own and realise what an exhausting job it is!

Seeking help
Sometimes, all of this may not be enough and the family (or the adolescent) may be unable to cope.

Worries about the physical changes of adolescence – are they too early, too late or ever going to happen – or about relationships can be discussed with the family doctor.

When problems arise at school, obviously teachers may be a useful source of information. The teacher may suggest that an educational psychologist becomes involved. Psychologists can find out if there are any particular problems with learning, but can also offer counselling if relationships are the issue.

Adolescents who experience turmoil or distress for more than a few months – persistent depression, anxiety, serious eating disorders or difficult behaviour – generally require outside help. Counselling agencies may be suitable if things have not gone too far. They exist for young people and for parents.

However, specialist help may be needed from the Child and Adolescent Mental Health Services. They mainly offer out-patient treatment and can be contacted through the family doctor.

As they grow older, develop the desire for privacy and need to be less dependent, adolescents may, quite naturally, wish to see the doctor on their own. The law allows them to agree their own treatment from the age of 16, or younger under certain circumstances.

© Royal College of Psychiatrists
April, 1994

Why do young minds matter?

Mental health means much more than just the absence of mental illness. It is about physical and emotional well-being, about having the strength and capacity to live a full and creative life, and also the flexibility to deal with its ups and downs

What is special about the mental health of children?

Childhood, from infancy through adolescence, is the time when mental health is developed. Apart from basic physical needs such as food and shelter, children need enough love and security to make them feel safe, happy and confident.

Whether these needs are fulfilled depends very much on how far the adults around young people (at home, at school and in the community) can look after them, and create the right conditions for them to form satisfactory relationships, to make the most of their abilities and talents and to prepare for taking on adult responsibilities.

What can go wrong?

Children can experience all sorts of pressures and difficulties.

Some problems can have a serious and significant effect on a young person's future

It is not easy for children and young people to grow up in today's complex society. There is so much that is going on: so many changes in values, new kinds of pressures – at school or in employment, from TV, the media and worldwide events, and from family life in its many different forms. Most children cope well enough; with the backup of those around them they can enjoy and make the most of their opportunities.

Some however don't do so well.

Without the right circumstances and support, problems may arise which can have a significant effect on a young person's future and can potentially lead to serious difficulties.

Families may be under great strain coping with separation, divorce, or bereavement. Illness and disability suffered by the child or other members of the family may produce particular emotional difficulties. Perhaps there are housing problems or financial hardships. Young parents may lack support when they need it, and find themselves unable to look after their children as they would want to. Others may not be able to cope well enough to promote their children's growth and development, and neglect or abuse may result.

When things go wrong, children and young people can experience all kinds of difficulties. They may not sleep well, have nightmares or night fears, or wet the bed. They can have difficulties in learning or become disruptive in the classroom. They may become increasingly fussy about food or cleanliness, or as teenagers develop eating problems (such as anorexia or bulimia; Young Minds has a leaflet about these). They may become very sad and depressed and try to harm themselves, or even become suicidal. Perhaps they have trouble making friends, or find relationships at home increasingly difficult. Children can also become fearful, feel intimidated and resent what is expected of them. They may not want to grow up and take responsibility. Some withdraw. Others become aggressive, attacking authority, being destructive, getting into fights and trouble.

What can be done to help?

When young people are emotionally troubled, parents may need to seek professional help.

When problems of this kind persist – to the point where children become very distressed, confused or out of control, and where family and friends feel that they can't manage or get through any more – then it is time to think about seeking professional help. You can be put in touch with the most appropriate support through your GP, social worker, teacher or health visitor, and sometimes parents or young people can refer themselves to a service.

Whether it is a specific problem or something more general, there are people who specialise in helping and understanding troubled children and young people, and their families. For example, at Child and Family Consultation Services (or Child Guidance Units – there is a Young Minds leaflet about these), specially trained professionals are available, such as psychiatrists, psychologists, psychotherapists, social workers, doctors, nurses, counsellors and occupational therapists. In some areas, parents or young people may telephone or walk in for information and/or an appointment without a formal referral. However, if a child under 16 approaches the service, it is usual for the parents or carers to be contacted should further help be required.

Other services are confidential (particularly youth counselling centres); young people can ask about this. Voluntary organisations and helplines can sometimes provide information and support, and suggest ways of getting help.

Young Minds, the National Association for Child and Family Mental Health, has more information about mental health problems, mental health professionals and services. We have a database of resources which can help you identify appropriate services in your area.

Mental illness

Sometimes I think I can't go on any more . . .

It's a feeling you may recognise. Things are getting you down and piling on top of you – you begin to feel there's no escape. Nothing you do seems to make a difference. The pressures keep building up and you feel incapable of getting out from under them. The present can seem meaningless, the future hopeless.

Suicidal thoughts are more common than you think

At some point you may feel that you can't go on any more and even have thoughts of ending it all. When they occur, suicidal thoughts are frightening and may also add to the pressure you feel under – 'I must be crazy to think like that.' But suicidal thoughts are much more common than you think and, in fact, many of us have them at some point in our lives. They are a sign that you need to take stock of what is happening to you and do something about it. It is likely that you are becoming depressed and need some help to get over it.

Getting help

If you are feeling down and start to have suicidal thoughts, close friends and relatives can be a source of support, but they need to know how you are feeling to be able to help. Simply talking things over can often be the best release. Sometimes, however, your family or friends may not be able or know how to help.

You may feel that you have no friend or relative around at the moment with whom you feel comfortable talking. If you think about it, you will usually find that there is someone, perhaps an old friend or relative you haven't seen in a while. Or perhaps there is a counselling service at your place of work to which you can turn. It is also worth remembering that The Samaritans are always available – day and night – to offer a confidential 'listening ear.'

General practitioners, in particular, are an excellent source of help because they are trained to know what to do when someone becomes depressed. You may find it easiest to approach your family doctor whom you may have known for many years. If on the other hand you prefer to see a different doctor, all general practitioners are equipped to help. Alternatively, contact the Health Information Service free on 0800 66 55 44 and they will put you in touch

---

But suicidal thoughts are much more common than you think and, in fact, many of us have them at some point in our lives

---

with GPs in your area. If you are not registered, go to your nearest surgery and the staff there will help you to do so.

Doctors are there to help you – don't feel guilty about going to see them

You mustn't feel that you are wasting your doctor's time by consulting him or her. Feeling depressed and suicidal is as painful as most physical illnesses and is just as deserving of help. You may feel that the situation you are in is your fault and that it is your responsibility to sort it out, or just to keep your problems covered up. But we all have limits to how much we can work and cope with unpleasant feelings. Often, the more depressed and pent-up you feel, the less able you are to deal with your situation. Fortunately, it is possible to get help whatever the source of your distress or depression.

Suicide

There has been a lot of research into suicide and the circumstances under which it occurs. Generally, however, most people's understanding of it is poor. In some ways that's understandable: after all, it is not a topic with which many people feel comfortable. But if we are to do something about it, public awareness needs to be increased.

Depression is a treatable condition

We do know that suicide is usually an act only carried out by someone who is depressed. Nine out of ten people who commit suicide have some form of mental health problem – the 'rational suicide' is rare. But depression is generally treatable given time, even in the face of seemingly overwhelming life events and circumstances.

What sort of depression symptoms do you need to look for?

Symptoms of depression include feeling low and a belief that things will not improve. Physical symptoms include a loss of appetite, sometimes with weight loss, and irregular sleep patterns, particularly waking early. The sufferer may lose interest in his or her usual hobbies and activities, withdraw from social contacts, become irritable, or think about suicide.

If someone really wants to commit suicide, won't they do it anyway?

No. All sorts of things can intervene to make someone think again about suicide: life circumstances can change unexpectedly or people can find ways of viewing them more positively, either on their own or with help from friends, relatives or employers. Treatment for depression, too, can help people to look at life differently and find the energy and drive to tackle problems which may have seemed overwhelming. Getting help is the most important step in combating depression and suicidal feelings.

But surely people who talk about it never do it?

Sadly, the reverse is the case. Over two-thirds of those who commit suicide have talked in general terms about it with someone, and at least a third have talked about actually doing it.

Two-thirds visit their doctor in the month before their suicide – 40 per cent in the previous week – but often they haven't talked directly about the source of their troubles.

Threats of suicide by adolescents should be taken seriously, particularly

---

Suicide is as common as deaths from road traffic accidents. That means over 5,000 deaths in England each year – an average of one every two hours

---

if they talk of feeling hopeless as well as depressed. Young adolescents are particularly vulnerable; far fewer contact their doctor or other advice agency than do older adolescents and adults.

If you try to talk with someone about suicide, aren't they more likely to do it?

There is no evidence to suggest that asking someone about suicide makes it more likely. But not talking or asking about it may leave the person feeling more isolated and unable to express their feelings. Simply ignoring someone's distress can prevent that person from getting help at an early stage. So it is important that we all understand what we can do to help – as a friend, relative or employer.

How common is suicide?

Suicide is as common as deaths from road traffic accidents. That means over 5,000 deaths in England each year – an average of one every two hours. This rate has not changed appreciably in the last few years, although there was a slight drop in numbers in the 1970s when natural gas was introduced into domestic homes, replacing poisonous coal gas.

Are some people more at risk than others?

Suicide is very rare under the age of 14. Some adolescents are more at risk than others. These include those who are depressed, who misuse alcohol or other substances, who are in trouble with the law, and whose sexual orientation brings them into conflict with their family or others. Suicide is three times as common in men as in women – young men are particularly at risk.

The suicide rate is higher

---

amongst divorced people and lower in married people; higher amongst unskilled workers and the unemployed. Physical illness and social isolation are also factors. Older people are at greatest risk, particularly if they have been recently bereaved. The rate varies with the seasons and is more common in April, May and June.

Some occupational groups are more at risk than others. The high-risk groups tend to be those with ready access to guns or drugs. Suicide amongst farmers is particularly high. In recognition of this problem, farmers' organisations have set up special support networks. For similar reasons, doctors and vets have been looking at establishing different sources of support. Prisoners are also a major cause of concern and the Prison Service has developed suicide prevention policies with which to combat the problem.

Suicide rates are also much higher amongst those with some form of mental illness than in the general population. Ten per cent of people with schizophrenia eventually die from suicide, as well as 15 per cent of those with depressive illnesses and a similar figure for those with personality disorders or a dependence on alcohol.

Why is the rate particularly high amongst young men?

Between 1982 and 1991, the suicide rate in young men aged 15 to 24 rose by 75 per cent. Personal financial and job circumstances are recognised as amongst the factors which may increase the risk of suicide. However, these can only be regarded as part of a more complex problem.

Another factor affecting the rate may be the much higher consumption of alcohol and drugs by young men. In addition, ready access to motor vehicles may explain why carbon monoxide poisoning from car exhaust fumes is the most common method that they use.

By contrast, the suicide rate for young women has fallen over the years. Motherhood may be one factor that protects women from actual suicide, although it doesn't protect them against depression which usually precedes it.

If someone has attempted suicide once or twice and not succeeded, how long are they still at risk?

The extent of a person's risk after a suicide attempt depends very much on the individual and his or her circumstances, the seriousness of the attempt, and the amount of care and support available afterwards. But the fact remains that the raised risk does last for quite a long time. A person who has tried to commit suicide is estimated to be a hundred times more at risk than the general population for the first year after the attempt. The doctor, nurse, psychologist or social worker who has seen the person concerned will be able to tell you more about the risk to that particular individual.

What can we do to prevent suicide?

Safety measures and education have helped to reduce deaths from road traffic accidents despite an increase in the amount of traffic on the road. Similarly, we can expect action and understanding to reduce suicide rates. It is important that we do as much to develop ways of preventing suicide as we do to prevent other significant causes of death. For this reason, the government's strategy for health, 'The Health of the Nation,' has set targets to reduce suicide.

There are now a number of agencies and support groups to which individuals can turn when they feel depressed or anxious. The Samaritans can be contacted at any hour of the day or night and they offer time and befriending. Other organisations like the Manic Depression Fellowship, MIND and SANE can also offer support. Compassionate Friends and CRUSE can provide help and support to those who have been bereaved, including those bereaved by suicide. Please see the list of telephone numbers and addresses on page 39.

Young people with worries can also talk to a member of the school staff, and they can always telephone the local child guidance clinic and ask to speak to one of the professional staff there, or talk to their school nurse or doctor.

More important, however, is the early recognition of relatives and friends who might be at risk, and the identification and treatment of underlying problems like depression. It is vital that you treat anyone's talk of suicide very seriously, however young or old they may be – that in itself can help. If in doubt about the seriousness of a situation, talk to someone with more knowledge, such as The Samaritans or your doctor. You may need to arrange for the individual concerned to be with someone until appropriate treatment is given.

For yourself, keep mentally healthy:
- Make sure you have effective ways of relaxing – music, sport, seeing friends, etc.
- Learn a relaxation technique for those times when you are in the middle of a meeting, surrounded by screaming kids, or up a ladder and are getting particularly frustrated.
- Don't take on too much, especially when under stress.
- Sit back and review your situation occasionally, particularly how you use your time.
- Take a break every so often – you'll work better when you get back to what you've been doing.
- Try not to cut yourself off from other people – keep in contact with friends, neighbours and family.
- Do seek support – talk things over – before things get too bad.
- Get enough sleep. If you don't, and maybe it and other things are getting you down, get some help from your doctor.

Prepared by the Department of Health

Mental health on the streets

- Approximately one-third of homeless people have mental health problems. Confounding popular myth, very few of them have, in fact, been released from psychiatric hospitals (follow-up reports show that most of these people were found some sort of secure accommodation).
- 50 per cent of the clients seen by the initiative have very severe mental health problems.
- There have been 34 homicides by mentally ill people in the past three years but they are much more likely to hurt themselves. One hundred and seven former psychiatric patients discharged from hospital killed themselves between September 1992 and September 1993. Statistically, you are far more likely to be killed by your partner than by someone who is homeless with mentally ill problems.
- In the next couple of weeks, the Zito Trust will get full charity status. Set up last July by Michael Howlett and Jayne Zito, whose husband was stabbed to death by Christopher Clunis, a schizophrenic who had seen 33 different agencies in the community, the Trust aims to provide support for victims of the failures of Care in the Community.
- Hospitals and medication account for 77 per cent of the NHS mental health budget.
- Last month a report by a team led by Sir Louis Blom-Cooper QC, into the death of occupational therapist Georgina Robinson at the hands of a patient at the Torbay General Hospital made the case for introducing compulsory treatment as part of comprehensive care plans for patients.
- On January 24 1995 Dulwich MP Tessa Jowell presented the Community Care (Rights) Bill in Parliament. Drafted by mental health charity MIND, the Bill proposes to provide 24-hour crisis care for people diagnosed as mentally ill, giving them the level of support they need to live in the community.

© The Big Issue February, 1995

Met rethink on mentally ill

**Dealing with the mentally ill is now part of everyday policework.
Tony Thompson reports.**

The Metropolitan Police Service is to provide 22,900 of its officers with comprehensive training in how to deal with the increasing numbers of mentally ill people they encounter on the capital's streets.

The initiative is a direct response to the perceived failure of the Government's Care in the Community programme, and also to last year's report on the 1992 murder of Jonathan Zito by schizophrenic Christopher Clunis, which criticised the police for being unco-ordinated and for 'failing to protect the public from potential harm'.

According to unofficial estimates, each month officers in the five police divisions currently deal with around 1,800 people with mental disorders, the vast majority of whom have a history of mental illness but have, like Clunis, been discharged into the community. The true figure is believed to be far higher as most police encounters with the mentally ill do not actually involve a crime and are therefore not recorded.

Previously, training in how to deal with the mentally disturbed was limited to an 80-minute lecture during an officer's initial 20-week training stint at Hendon. Under the new programme, all ranks, from constable to inspector, will have to complete a correspondence course which will focus on legislation, local practice and procedures. It will explain the role of other agencies and inform officers of the pitfalls of making unnecessary arrests and prosecutions.

Officers will also attend a one-day seminar hosted by local mental health professionals and watch a new video, 'A Meeting of Minds – A Positive Response to Mental Disorder.'

Each police division will also appoint a full-time liaison officer – a response to an internal, two-year study which found that the majority of officers were reluctant to deal with the mentally ill, seeing such work as tiresome, time-consuming and a distraction from the main task of catching villains.

> *Previously, training in how to deal with the mentally disturbed was limited to an 80-minute lecture during an officer's initial 20-week training stint at Hendon*

The problem is exacerbated by a lack of facilities for the mentally ill in the capital. The report on the Clunis incident called for more beds in medium-secure units in south-east London, while another report on mental care services in north-west London said the system was cracking under the strain.

Bed occupancy levels in all the capital's acute psychiatric hospital wards are currently running at well over 100 per cent. This places additional pressure on the police, who are often unable to ensure those they find are given the support and treatment which they require.

Last week two of London's top psychiatrists condemned the 'dangerous deterioration' of mental health care in the capital. Professor Steven Hirsch and Dr Cosmo Hallstrom warned that at the current rate of decline, no beds at all would be available by 2000.

A spokeswoman for SANE, the mental health charity, welcomed the police initiative, saying the programme showed sensitivity and insight into what was becoming an increasing problem. 'The number of mentally disordered people who present a genuine risk is minimal, but the police are at the forefront of protecting and assessing those who have been discharged into the community. This programme will aid them in that task.'

*© Time Out
January, 1995*

Antidepressants

Your questions answered

In the wake of The Royal College of Psychiatrists' Defeat Depression Action Week in March, here are MIND's responses to the questions about antidepressant drugs that are most frequently asked of us at MIND's Information Service.

Q *Are antidepressants useful?*

A They can be. If someone is stuck in depression they may not be able to benefit from any 'talking treatments' that may be available. MIND takes the view that people should be given informed choice about any treatment offered and should be provided with a range of options as appropriate. For further information see MIND's leaflet *Understanding Depression* available from MIND Mail Order.

Q *Do antidepressants have any side effects?*

A All drugs have some unwanted effects: antidepressants are no exception. The unwanted effects of antidepressants vary according to the subgroup to which they belong as well as the particular drug's characteristics.

Q *What are the main differences between these groups of antidepressants?*

A There are three main groups: 1) tricyclics and newer related antidepressants, 2) MAOIs, 3) SSRIs plus a couple of odd ones that have particular characteristics, namely amoxapine and moclobemide. The older ones (tricyclics and MAOIs) are more sedating than others and have more unwanted effects on the heart and circulatory system. They can be very dangerous if more than the prescribed dose is taken. If you are prescribed MAOIs then you have to avoid eating certain foods as a dangerous reaction can occur, which means that MAOIs are not prescribed

so often. The newer SSRIs have their own pattern of unwanted effects ranging from nausea to nervousness but these may be less of a problem than some of the older antidepressants.

Q *Is there an antidepressant that is better than the others?*

A A disadvantage of all antidepressants is that they all take roughly two to four weeks to take effect. None have been proven to work more quickly. All have some unwanted effects.

Some antidepressants may have unwanted effects that are hazardous for particular groups of people or individuals (e.g. sedating drugs for people who have to drive, or ones which can cause low blood pressure and dizziness, which might lead to falls and broken bones in elderly people, or ones that are particularly hazardous in overdose for people who may be suicidal). But individual responses to drugs differ and you would need to discuss your particular needs with your doctor.

Q *How does my doctor choose which antidepressant to prescribe?*

A Your doctor will bear in mind any medical condition you suffer from and any other drugs you may be taking; any adverse effects or any benefits you may have experienced if you have taken antidepressants before; whether sedation is useful or a disadvantage (e.g. calming anxiety versus the need to be able to work). Some of the newer antidepressants are more expensive to prescribe and this may deter some doctors from prescribing them.

Q *How long would I need to stay on an antidepressant drug?*

A This very much depends on how you respond to antidepressants. Research indicates that staying on antidepressants for six months after they have started working for you cuts down the risk of further episodes of depression. Your doctor may therefore prefer you to keep taking the antidepressants for this period of time. You would need to take antidepressants on a regular basis. They don't work if just taken on 'off days' or irregularly.

Q   *Are antidepressants addictive?*

A   Broadly speaking, most antidepressants are not addictive in the sense that minor tranquillisers are, but a lot more is known about the older antidepressants that have been on the market a long time. A few individual antidepressants, because of their particular stimulant effect may carry a risk of dependency, (namely the MAOI tranylcypromine, amoxapine and possibly the new antidepressant moclobemide). People may find it harder to stop taking these ones.

There is however a pattern of mainly physical effects that you may temporarily experience on stopping all antidepressants, especially if you suddenly stop taking them, so it is better to gradually reduce the dose.

Q   *What sort of symptoms might I get on stopping antidepressants?*

A   This pattern ranges from flu-like symptoms to restlessness, disturbed sleep and jitteriness.

Q   *How long might this withdrawal pattern last?*

A   We wouldn't expect it to last more than a month at most, probably a lot less than this.

For further information see MIND's booklet *Making Sense of Treatments and Drugs: Antidepressants* available from MIND Mail Order. Address details on page 39.

One in seven adults hit by mental disorder

More than six million people are suffering from neurotic disorders, according to official figures released yesterday. One in seven adults is blighted by depression, anxiety or some other kind of psychological disorder, the figures showed.

Sufferers were often plagued by fatigue, sleep problems, irritability and worry. Women were more likely to be victims. This snapshot of the nation's mental health was revealed in one of the largest surveys on mental illness.

The study by the Office of Population, Censuses and Surveys was jointly commissioned by the Department of Health, the Scottish Home and Health Office and the Welsh Office.

Interviews were carried out with 10,000 adults plus 350 people suffering from psychosis, 1,200 in psychiatric hospitals and 1,100 living in hostels or sleeping rough.

Sufferers were often plagued by fatigue, sleep problems, irritability and worry

---

People were asked if they suffered any of 14 symptoms over the past month and to give details of their frequency and severity. The symptoms – all indicators of varying degrees of mental illness – were fatigue, sleep problems, irritability, worry, anxiety, obsessions, depression and depressive ideas, including thoughts of suicide.

Lack of concentration and forgetfulness, unexplained aches or pains brought on by stress, compulsions, phobias, worries about physical health and panic or fear of losing control were also measured.

Preliminary findings showed the most common neurotic problem was a mixed anxiety and depressive disorder, affecting 7.1 per cent. Next, at 3 per cent, was a generalised anxiety disorder.

Severe disorders, such as schizophrenia and manic depression, affect four people in 1,000 every year, researchers estimated.

The number of people found to be dependent on alcohol and drugs was 4.7 per cent and 2.2 per cent respectively, with men three times as likely to be alcoholics as women and twice as likely to have a drug problem.

Three experiences of madness

Sometimes a psychotic illness, in addition to pain and turmoil, can bring some richness, some self-knowledge. Three sufferers describe their experiences of the journey through the dark portals

The lawyer's tale:
by Daniel Levy

I was a happy child. I attended a direct grant grammar school in West London, during which time I obtained creditable O and A levels. I was fortunate enough to be admitted to Oxford University, where I studied law and narrowly missed obtaining first class honours.

I arranged solicitors' articles at a well known City of London firm. However, during my time at solicitors' college, I began to suffer from depression. I postponed the solicitors' final examination and started my articles.

The depression became so intense that I was forced to leave the firm. After a few months, I was admitted to hospital and eventually diagnosed as suffering from manic depression.

Manic depression is one of the major mental illnesses for which, at present, there is no cure. I have spent three lengthy spells in hospital of which the last, in 1988–89 was eight months.

I can clearly remember that when I was first mentally ill, my mother was frequently in tears, and my father had some particularly bad asthma attacks.

I now realise how difficult it must have been for my family to cope with me.

Many mental illnesses, and most particularly schizophrenia, start in a person's late teens. The family often has to decide whether behaviour such as staying in bed for most of the day, lack of cleanliness, refusal to eat properly, or saying strange things are the result of mental illness, or merely adolescent rebellion.

The first step is usually to seek advice from the GP who may do one of several things: nothing at all; prescribe medication, arrange a consultation with a psychiatrist, or advise immediate admission to hospital. I was fortunate. Our family doctor is a wise and knowledgeable man who recognised how ill I was. The trouble is that many GPs know very little about mental illness and often make inaccurate diagnoses.

Another problem is that people with severe mental illness are often unaware they are ill and refuse to see the family doctor. If persuasion fails, it is hard to know how to break this impasse and get them there. It may be that someone who refuses to see the doctor on the grounds that he is not ill will be more willing to talk to someone who is less overtly medical, such as a psychiatric social worker or a community psychiatric nurse.

Another big problem is obtaining hospital treatment for the sufferer. Admission to hospital may be as a voluntary patient or under a section of the Mental Health Act 1983. Most patients (over 90 per cent) are admitted on a voluntary basis, but if the sufferer needs medical treatment, and refuses it, he may be 'sectioned' and admitted compulsorily for assessment or treatment.

I have been sectioned on several occasions and was never informed of my right to appeal against it. Many of a person's rights are curtailed when they are 'under section', especially that of being able to refuse medical treatment. I still remember that while under section I was frequently locked for many hours in a seclusion room which was very dark and without furniture except for a mattress on the floor.

Some mental illnesses involve the sufferer becoming psychotic. It can happen either before or during hospital treatment. Psychosis is a state of mind involving delusions. Essentially the sufferer is in another world, hearing and seeing things which no-one else can hear or see, shouting in reply to the imaginary voices which assail him.

I spent long periods suffering with psychosis. I

Photo: SANE

I now realise how difficult it must have been for my family to cope with me.

remember thinking I was the Prime Minister, a Disraeli-like figure. And, of course, I was a relative of the Queen. While I was psychotic I would often ignore my family when they came to visit me. To begin with I tried to talk to them, but when I found they did not believe my delusions of grandeur, I decided they really weren't worth conversing with. A Prime Minister had better things to do!

It is hard for the family to help someone who is living in this world of delusion, but they should listen to the sufferer and acknowledge how real the delusions appear without colluding with him. Although psychotic illness cannot be cured, distressing delusions can be controlled by the antipsychotic drugs. The trouble is that many people on their own in the community think they no longer need their medication, soon relapse and then decide they are not ill.

I have been fortunate because my family discussed how I should be cared for after leaving hospital and what symptoms to watch for. People who live on their own are much less fortunate.

Mental illness is, alas, often long and drawn out, and destroys one's ambitions and those of your family for you and dashes hopes of a sparkling career. The majority of chronic mental illnesses are incompatible with the pressures that much employment involves. People with manic depression can take heart from the fact that Winston Churchill, Virginia Woolf, Sylvia Plath and many more brilliantly creative and artistic people were sufferers.

But for more ordinary people, the person who is ill suffers most from the stigma and becomes unemployable. The family has to accept that the career the sufferer trained for is no longer within his grasp. Perhaps it is time to change the law to improve employment prospects for the mentally ill. Perhaps the family, through their kindness and understanding, can help their stricken son or daughter and persuade them to accept that, for the present, their chance of following their chosen employment has gone. For myself, I work happily as a volunteer for Saneline.

The musician's tale: by Ben Silcock

I want to try to shed a little light on the experience of madness from the point of view of the afflicted. So often we get descriptions of madness from psychiatrists who can only express their observations in a clinical way, with little consideration for the patient's soul.

There are two enemies waiting in the wings – paranoia and violence

Mine is a strictly personal viewpoint, and I shall try to describe the direct experience of what it is like to be mad. I shall also say something about the view from a sane perspective, and looking back towards past madness.

So we find the afflicted outside and wandering God know where. He's got an angel on one shoulder and a demon on the other. A couple of days ago he had a vision, perhaps of Christ, but he only knows that something extremely powerful has

---

Music trance

Close my eyes
feel my arms tightly folded
listening close my head loves
the room stretches
    wide over a
dark blue lamp into clear
    black expanse
full of life
shimmering grey pink orange
    everything peace
quiet no sound but beat
    in my head
time no longer moves as
    I fly with it
without moving becoming
    the clear dark
Oh such peace so huge
    never ending
I love the truth behind my
    eyes that feel open
I feel so big but oh so small.
James Scott

---

touched him – and so he goes out and walks miles and miles trying to find salvation and meaning.

What I am trying to say is that a maddened person has not just copped out of living an ordinary existence, he (or she) has somehow met with an experience so extremely potent that he is unable to focus on normality until he has been able to make sense of what's hit him – a psychological thunderbolt.

Unfortunately, in the case of the afflicted, the experience may well be religious, but it is not always peaceful. There are two enemies waiting in the wings – paranoia and violence. Now I don't know how paranoia comes into being, but I do know the more paranoid you get, the more violence rears its ugly head, and can actually consume you.

Anyway, for all your strange behaviour, in the end the various authorities catch up with you, and the corridors of the mental hospital yawn at you.

At this stage it is easy to feel the confinements and injections of the mental health people are really the devil trying to destroy your religious convictions. All the experiences and feelings you got at the outset seem to be crushed by well meaning staff.

However, once the hospital has worked for a while on you, hopefully there is a coming down to earth, and normal rationality returns. The various staff become doctors and nurses instead of 1984-type thought police.

Coming down can be one of the most painful parts: no doubt you may have done some dreadful things during the days of turmoil, as well as feeling frightened and depressed after such a trauma.

So once you are back to sanity, what happens? Hospital becomes a good place to be; for after being so shaken up it's vital to be in a situation where there is some protection. In a hospital one can recover without the impersonal big wide world and all its stressful ways. Also hospitals provide activities that can help you come to terms with your life again.

Personally, I would say that when looking back at periods of lunacy, I don't just think, 'Oh, I've been ill,' I'd say: 'Something happened to me – something I can't explain.' There is no way I can just call it illness: but I can call it madness.

So somehow you've got to get back into the world and function as best you can. I can only speak for myself, but I do know others who have had similar experiences. In material terms one probably isn't doing so well, but to be positive, your unconscious has opened up in some way, and there is food for thought in self-knowledge.

You see, going back to the beginning when the powers that be touched you is something that I don't think will ever leave you despite all the clinical theories. I suppose our materialistic existence in this day and age is not a good bed for soul experience to rest on. By this I mean that confusion, turmoil and madness can be sparked off when the spiritual touches the material: maybe we should take a break-down as a sign that our ways of living need to change.

The surveyor's tale: by John Tennant

About sixteen years ago, when I was aged 24 years, and had just qualified as a surveyor, I took a job as an estate agent in Southampton. I wasn't very good at it, and due to lack of sales, was asked to leave the company after working a month there. I suppose it was not very surprising. I was quite a 'mixed up' person in many ways with real problems relating to people. Then, a few days before leaving, I had picked up a rugby injury, concussion, and I was starting to get very depressed. In fact, I had become a nervous wreck.

On my last day at work, I shook hands with everybody. I remember one man who disliked me leered into my eyes as he shook hands and I felt something snap in my head. I thought nothing of it at the time and went back to my flat to pack in order to return to my parents in London.

For the next couple of weeks I got more and more depressed. Then, one night, when I was in deep sleep, I was suddenly aware that a pair of green eyes was staring into my eyes from behind my head. Lights came from the eyes and the inside of my head lit up. I then had a massive fit.

Two vicious circular twists shook my brain, and my face and body shook and contorted.

During this time I was feeling my lifeforce slipping away. My mother, hearing my screams, turned on the light in my room and, I believe, saved my life. It was 2 am and I was shaking uncontrollably with fear. The GP was called and I was taken to a local psychiatric hospital. It was extremely frightening to be admitted there for the first time. I felt desperately lonely and suicidal. The doctors who saw me did not smile reassuringly at me when we talked. It was as if they knew a secret that I didn't know at the time. Maybe I had an incurable illness that I would have to learn to live with?

I have discovered the need to remain grounded and in touch with the wonder of everyday life

The diagnosis was made that I was suffering from paranoid schizophrenia. Looking back it seems that I was given this illness by a madman who either wanted to teach me a lesson or kill me.

It was then that I began to hear voices. The fact is that having heard them has had a profound effect on me. When your mind has reached out to touch the universe, you are never quite the same. I would say I am a much kinder person now, more caring and socially aware. I am aware of the power of art, music and spirituality in my life. I have also discovered the healing power which comes from the sharing of feelings and emotions. Through severe hardship I have discovered the need to remain grounded and in touch with the wonder of everyday life. Social skills have developed too and deep friendships have blossomed.

I have made quite a lot of progress. My mood swings, anxiety and depression have gone. So have the voices. However, I have had to be readmitted to hospital a further four times. I have investigated a wide range of therapies and work opportunities. I have been encouraged to explore my creativity: artistic, spiritual, writing and music.

I still take an injection of Piportil every four weeks. The physical and psychological effects of the illness have largely gone now, although I still have to take it easy.

It has been a terrible struggle, but, as I said to a friend recently: 'I have finished blaming others for my disappointments. My life is in my own hands now.'

The above is an extract from *Sanetalk*, the magazine published by Sane. For more details, see address on page 39.

© Sane, *Summer*, 1994

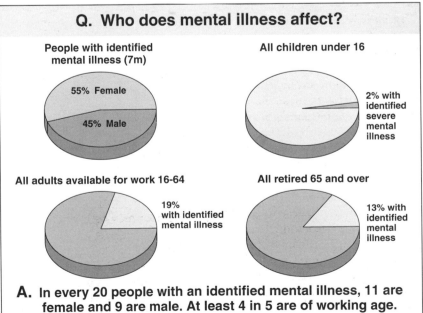

Q. Who does mental illness affect?

People with identified mental illness (7m)

55% Female
45% Male

All children under 16

2% with identified severe mental illness

All adults available for work 16-64

19% with identified mental illness

All retired 65 and over

13% with identified mental illness

A. In every 20 people with an identified mental illness, 11 are female and 9 are male. At least 4 in 5 are of working age.

From: *Mental Illness: The Fundamental Facts* published by The Mental Health Foundation

Time to jettison the Mental Health Act

Safety for patients and the public is a prerequisite in caring for the mentally ill, says Elaine Murphy

The publication of the South Devon Inquiry Report into the death of the social worker Georgina Robinson was merely the most recent to highlight the inadequate state of mental health services for people with severe mental illness. The South Devon service is, however, a good deal better overall than most in the UK.

This is the first time I can remember during my career when the key players in the mental health field all agree on the overall strategy. The problem is not the policy but its implementation, which is struggling woefully.

Need for services may be four to five times as great in deprived urban areas as more affluent suburban and rural areas, and yet distribution of resources takes no account whatever of this. Furthermore, money is fixed largely in hospital-based care, whereas service users and their families want a 24-hour, reliable, year-round community-based service – at the moment, in most districts, community care 'shuts up shop' outside office hours.

Patients want practical help and support, for example with housing, finance and employment, something to do during the day, and social relationships which give meaning to their lives. But at present they are often offered a monthly injection of drugs and little more.

Targeting of services is especially poor; many community psychiatric staff do not work with those with the most serious long-term problems; staffing of the services is dominated by health professionals (doctors, nurses), when what is required is an army of people to provide practical social care and help

– people who are far less expensive to employ but who, with the right training and support, are able to provide a more flexible type of service.

> **Patients want practical help and support. They are offered a monthly injection of drugs and little more.**

Hospital beds are used extraordinarily inefficiently – many admissions could be avoided if there were good, round-the-clock care at home, which most patients prefer even when they are seriously ill. A high proportion of beds are occupied by people who no longer need hospital care but do need long-term support.

There are two reasons for the catastrophic failure of community

care implementation. Until these are tackled, avoidable tragedies will continue to shock, and tens of thousands of patients and their families will find the burden of mental illness unrelieved. The first is the dearth of visionary leadership and effective management in mental health services, accompanied by a lack of understanding by health and local authorities of the sheer enormity of the changes that have to be made in order to target the services at people with long-term serious mental illness.

The Government is aware of this and has recently, through the NHS Executive and Training Division, invested £100,000 in a joint initiative to launch a series of training events for managers in London. This programme and other similar initiatives are vital, but they alone will not bring about the management revolution the public has a right to demand.

The second important change must be to the legal framework for

In most districts, community care 'shuts up shop' outside office hours

community care. The current Mental Health Act works against the possibility of caring effectively for patients in the community. The 1983 Act's underlying theme is that care and treatment for people who require compulsory care necessitates detention in hospital. It is obvious, however, that specific treatment, for example, monthly medication, can be administered in one licensed place, perhaps a day centre or doctor's surgery, and the person obliged to live and be cared for elsewhere in a specified place, such as a supervised hostel, residential home or their own home.

The second philosophical flaw in the 1983 Act is the removal of medical treatment from the social context of care. The Act focuses not on patients but on doctors. Successful care from the patient's point of view, however, enables him or her to lead as normal a life in the community as possible. Other aspects of care and supervision – such as a good relationship with a key member of staff, a place to live, social opportunities and adequate financial support – are prerequisites of rehabilitation.

The radical transformation of mental health services over the past decade, from being hospital-based to community-focused, should surely now be reflected in legislation. The stigmatising notion that incarceration is a necessary precondition for effective care should be dropped. There will, of course, often be times when detention in a secure place is necessary in the interests of safety for the general public, and that place will frequently be a secure hospital ward. But there are many other patients who can be treated satisfactorily in their own homes or in hostels, group homes, registered care homes and so on.

The radical transformation of mental health services over the past decade should surely now be reflected in legislation.

Compulsory admission powers are used sparingly, and often very late in a relapse, because of the traumatic disruption to the patient's life and the disquieting sense of failure for the professionals involved in the event. Compulsory admission to hospital should surely be reserved for those patients whose conditions are unresponsive to treatment and who have a specific need for very safe or secure care.

The problems inherent in the 1983 Act affect the care of a wide range of seriously mentally disordered people, not just the small, seriously 'at risk' group to which the patients at the centre of recent, well publicised tragedies belong.

The principles on which a new mental health Act should be constructed should provide a more therapeutic framework for care, continue to control the unwarranted interventions of doctors, and yet provide more safety and security for patients, their families and the general public. Adopting these principles, one could devise a power for the compulsory care of seriously mentally disordered people.

This broader concept of a comprehensive care plan order, in which specific medical treatment could be given compulsorily only in the context of a wider plan of supervision and care, would protect patients' welfare, particularly while they were receiving medication against their wishes.

The time has come to jettison an Act which neither protects the public effectively nor provides the care which seriously mentally disordered people require to achieve a more fulfilled and happier life.

© *The Independent*
January, 1995

Suicide facts

Every two hours someone in Britain commits suicide. Translated onto a global scale, an estimated 1,000 people a day (nearly one a minute) take their own lives.[1] Suicide accounts for around 40,000 deaths in the European Community each year. There are differences between EC countries in terms of suicide rates, with Denmark having the highest suicide rate followed by Belgium and France. The lowest rates are in Italy and Greece.[2] What appears to be a north-south suicide divide may reflect the fact that suicide is still one of the least acknowledged causes of death and cultural and religious inhibitions may deter many bereaved relatives from acknowledging suicides. Suicide ranks in the top ten causes of death throughout Europe – Austria, Hungary and Switzerland have extremely high rates – and is the second highest cause of mortality in young men.[3]

The known suicide rate is a considerable underestimate of the actual rate of suicide. The main reason for this disparity in Britain is because official statistics are based on coroners' verdicts. In the case of a suspected suicide an inquest will be held, but the victim's intention to commit suicide must be strictly proven. In the absence of any clear proof of intent, the verdict cannot be suicide; instead it is likely to be classified as 'death by misadventure,' 'accidental death,' or there will be an 'open' verdict. In an endeavour to protect relatives from stigma and distress, some coroners may be less inclined than others to pass verdicts of suicide. When the evidence is heard by a jury, they too can be reluctant to return a verdict of suicide: 'An examination of inquests in Inner North London found that juries hearing cases of deaths on the London Underground returned suicide verdicts in only some 40 per cent of these cases, despite the fact that the common assumption must be that all such deaths are suicidal.'[4]

The true rate of suicide in Britain has been estimated as far higher than the official statistics would suggest: 'Professor Norman Kreitman, an expert on the epidemiology of suicide, speaking on a radio programme in 1986, suggested that the actual rate was probably about 60 per cent higher than the official statistics. A recent study by Chambers and Harvey (1989) indicates that it may be more than double the published figures.'[5]

Most recently a north London coroner, Dr David Paul, commented that official suicide statistics are 'lies' that greatly underestimate the number of people who take their own lives. He said that 'coroners have been "hamstrung" by High Court rulings on inquests which now require that the proof that a person intended to take his or her own life be of the same standard as proof in a criminal trial . . . If we are looking at suicides as a reflection of social trends – such as unemployment and mental illness – then the suicide statistics in this country are total lies and are probably wrong by 30, 40, 50 per cent.'[6]

The gender gap

Suicide is consistently twice as common in men as in women.[1] However, women attempt suicide three times more often than men. An OPCS report published in 1993 showed that there were 4,362 male suicides in 1991, a 27 per cent increase over the previous twelve years, while the number of women who committed suicide dropped by 32 per cent over the same period. The report stated that the male increase was most marked in the 15–44 age group.[2] Overall, suicide accounted for 13 deaths a day (4,745) in the UK in 1991 – approximately the same number of people who died in road accidents.[3]

The Samaritans recently blamed the rising male suicide rate on the growing pressures of modern life and

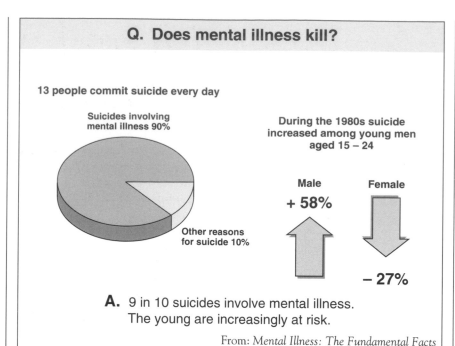

Q. Does mental illness kill?

13 people commit suicide every day

Suicides involving mental illness 90%

Other reasons for suicide 10%

During the 1980s suicide increased among young men aged 15 – 24

Male **+ 58%**

Female **– 27%**

A. 9 in 10 suicides involve mental illness. The young are increasingly at risk.

From: *Mental Illness: The Fundamental Facts*
Published by The Mental Health Foundation, £4.50

men's reluctance to discuss their feelings with those who might help them. They say fewer women commit suicide because they have an 'increased degree of self-worth' and a better ability to express emotion, which enables them to cope with major life crises and stress.[4] One psychiatrist, Dr Keith Hawton, has suggested that 'changes in society may have resulted in young men becoming less integrated with and supported by those around them with the reverse pattern for women.'[5]

The true rate of suicide in Britain has been estimated as far higher than the official statistics would suggest

---

If women really do have a greater sense of self-esteem, enjoy more opportunities for expressing their feelings and consequently suffer less alienation, it is surprising that the incidence of depression is approximately twice as high in women as in men. Also, an increasing number of women are attempting to kill themselves. In a study carried out by doctors at Warneford Hospital, Oxford which was published in '*The British Medical Journal*' in 1992, it

was estimated that 120,000 women between the ages of 15 and 35 attempt suicide in England and Wales each year. The authors concluded that deliberate overdosing had become the major reason for emergency medical admissions of women to hospital. More than ten per cent make a second attempt on their lives within a year.[6] Men tend to choose more violent methods of attempting suicide and are therefore more likely to succeed in killing themselves. A report by the Samaritans in 1992 showed that men are more likely to hang or poison themselves or use firearms.[7]

© *MIND*
1993

Sources:

1 '*A Special Scar – the Experiences of People Bereaved by Suicide*' by Alison Wertheimer. Tavistock / Routledge, 1991.

2 ECHO Health Data.

3 '*Implications for the Field of Mental Health of the European Targets for Attaining Health for All*'. World Health Organisation Regional Office for Europe, 1991.

4 '*Suicide*' by Susan Levey in '*Principles and Practice of Forensic Psychiatry*' edited by Robert Bluglass and Paul Bowden. Churchill Livingstone, 1990.

5 '*A special scar – the Experiences of People Bereaved by Suicide*', op cit.

6 *Coroner find rules limiting*, The Independent, 6 June 1991

Mental health and older people

Information from The Mental Health Foundation

What are mental health problems?

Problems such as feelings of depression, anxiety and confusion affect most people at some time, particularly after a distressing life event. Mental health problems arise when these symptoms occur to such an extent or for such a long period of time that they make it difficult to cope with everyday life.

Older people may be particularly vulnerable to such feelings, especially if they have suffered a bereavement, have problems with mobility or are feeling lonely or isolated. Older people are also far more at risk of developing some form of dementia.

How many older people are affected by mental health problems?

2 in 10 (10.6m) of the UK population are over retirement age – by the year 2000 1.2 million people will be over 85. An ageing population brings with it increasing rates of mental ill-health, particularly in the over 85 age group.

Five percent of all people over retirement age and 25% of people over 85 currently suffer from clinical dementia. 1.5 million people over 65 are affected by depression.

Studies show that only a quarter of dementia sufferers are known to GPs and 1 in 10 to psychiatrists. Virtually no depressed older people are known to GPs or to the psychiatric services.

How are older people affected by depression?

For some older people depression can be brought on by physical ill-health. The constant pain of arthritis and other conditions associated with ageing can leave people feeling desperately unhappy and isolated. GPs should always be consulted about medication and physiotherapy which can relieve many of the symptoms of these conditions and lead to greater independence and a better quality of life.

For other older people depression can be triggered by life changes such as bereavement or having to move into sheltered or residential accommodation or by loneliness or money worries.

Symptoms of depression include feelings of sadness which seem impossible to overcome and a loss of interest in life and activities. Motivation and drive can be lost as people feel that they do not have the energy to achieve even limited tasks. People can become withdrawn, have difficulty sleeping and even contemplate suicide. Anyone experiencing these feelings should talk to their GP as treatments and specialist sources of help are available.

What are the symptoms of dementia?

Symptoms vary between individuals, but initial problems usually relate to the loss of short-term memory. Sufferers may be able to remember events from the past, but have difficulty in remembering what they did only a few hours ago. They may also fail to recognise places or forget names of friends or family.

People with dementia often lose interest in their usual hobbies or pastimes and may appear apathetic or unmotivated. They can have difficulty grasping new ideas and so become frightened of change and unwilling to try new things.

Some people may also become moody or aggressive as they realise that they are no longer able to do things which in the past they have taken for granted.

Photo: David Hoffman

Older people may be particularly vulnerable

Who cares for older people with mental health problems?

Day centres and residential homes provide care for some people suffering from dementia or severe depression. However, as only 25% of dementia sufferers are known to GPs, the majority of people are cared for at home by family members. Research has shown that 1.6 million adults spend up to 20 hours a week caring for dependants with mental health problems in their own homes or other households.

Where can carers get support?

Carers should be in contact with their GP who can provide advice about medication and put them in touch with specialist services where necessary. GPs also have a responsibility to offer all patients an annual health check covering physical health and an assessment of mental functions such as memory and mood. If necessary, a GP can allocate a health visitor or district nurse to make home visits.

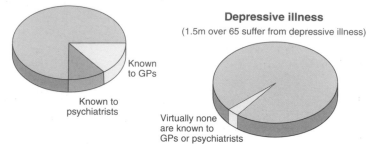

Q. Are we meeting the needs of older people with mental illness?

Dementia
(700,000 people over 65 suffer from dementia)

Known to GPs

Known to psychiatrists

Depressive illness
(1.5m over 65 suffer from depressive illness)

Virtually none are known to GPs or psychiatrists

A. Very few. Studies show that only 1 in 4 dementia sufferers are known to GPs. Virtually no depressed older people are known to GPs or the psychiatric services.

From: *Mental Illness: The Fundamental Facts* published by The Mental Health Foundation

Social Services Departments can also be contacted either directly or through a GP. They will carry out an assessment of needs and may assign a home help or offer a place at a day centre. Unlike GP services, social services such as these are not always provided free. Carers can find out what is available and what costs are involved through their GP or Local Authority.

Voluntary organisations are also able to offer advice and support and many have carer's support groups.

© The Mental Health Foundation
November, 1994

Depression in the workplace

The cost of depression

Introduction

Depression is a common illness. Some 20% of women and 10% of men can be expected to suffer from depression at some point during their lives.

One in twenty of all adults are estimated to be experiencing depression at any one time. Naturally problems that are common in the general population are common in people at work: the Department of Health and the Confederation of British Industry have estimated that between 15% and 30% of employees will experience some form of mental health problem during their working lives. As well as being a cause of untold distress, depression is linked to poor work performance and high rates of sickness absence, accidents and staff turnover.

What is depression?

People who have not suffered from depression do not know what it is like. Everyone may feel fed up, miserable or sad at certain times, particularly after deeply distressing occasions such as the death of a partner or relative. Usually this kind of sadness passes with time, but occasionally it may drag on or seem to get out of proportion to the unhappy event. Sometimes, unhappiness just comes 'out of the blue', without any obvious reason.

Depression is linked to poor work performance

Depression that persists, is severe, or that comes to dominate every aspect of the day, is an illness, and those affected will benefit from help.

Certain characteristic symptoms can give a clue that someone is suffering from depression that requires extra help. These may include:
- Sadness which does not change with circumstances.
- Crying for no apparent reason.
- Anxiety, worrying, irritability or tension.
- Disturbed sleep.
- Reduced appetite and loss of weight.
- Tiredness, lethargy and lack of motivation.
- Loss of interest in normal activities.

- Forgetfulness and inability to concentrate.
- Thoughts of worthlessness and hopelessness.

The effects of depression on work

Those suffering from depression will behave uncharacteristically in many aspects of their lives – at home and at work. Some features which may be-come particularly evident to fellow workers or to employers are:

- Slowness and mistakes in work.
- Poor concentration and forget-fulness.
- Poor time-keeping.
- Increase in unexplained absences or sick leave.
- Disputes and arguments with colleagues.

Depression can therefore have far reaching consequences for the ability of an employee to work effectively. Some of those affected by depression will have to stop work completely for a time because of the severity of their symptoms. Most, however, will attempt to soldier on, painfully aware that they are not performing as well as usual. Recognition that an individual is suffering from depres-sion, followed by effective help, will speed his or her return to normal performance at work as well as reducing much needless misery.

Recognition

Colleagues at work are in a good position to notice changes which may suggest that their workmate is suffering from depression, and should encourage them to seek help. An early decision to consult the occupational health department, or the family doctor, will allow earlier and more effective treatment. The manager or employer who is aware of an employee's difficulties can be helpful in allowing time off work if the depression is severe, as well as, in due course, encouraging and easing the employee's return to work. Of course, many employees will be afraid of disclosing problems which they fear may affect their job security, so this sensitive issue can often be handled effectively and confiden-tially by the occupational health adviser or the family doctor. Most

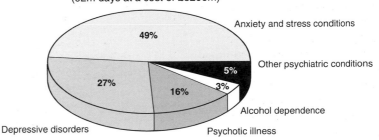

Q. How much does mental illness cost UK industry?

Working days due to mental illness
(92m days at a cost of £6200m)

- Anxiety and stress conditions — 49%
- Other psychiatric conditions — 5%
- Alcohol dependence — 3%
- Psychotic illness — 16%
- Depressive disorders — 27%

A. Days lost due to mental illness in the workforce cost UK industry £6200m in 1991. Sickness and invalidity benefits cost a further £1114m.

From: *Mental Illness: The Fundamental Facts* published by The Mental Health Foundation

people will be able to return to work within a few weeks.

Treatment

Talking about feelings is helpful in itself. Many people with depression will start to feel better once they have discussed their problems. The majority of people with depression will be helped more by a variety of treatments which can be provided by doctors or other trained pro-fessionals. Which treatment is most suitable will depend largely upon the individual as well as the nature of the depression. Most treatments fall into two main groups: talking treatments, such as counselling, and anti-depressant tablets, both of which are given as a course of treatment over a period of months. These can be used singly or together and will speed the recovery from a period of depression. Although there is a common worry that some of the drugs used in the treatment of depression can be addictive, there is in fact no evidence that this is the case. As with most other common illnesses, the majority of people will recover completely from depression and be able, in due course, to return to work as before.

Of great importance in the recovery from depression is the close working together of those providing help, including the family doctor, sometimes a psychiatrist specialising in the treatment of depression and the occupational health adviser who is aware of the demands and con-ditions of the workplace.

Can unsatisfactory working conditions cause depression?

For most people work provides a structure to the day and the oppor-tunity to make friendships as well as a way of increasing one's sense of self-worth and of feeling valued. For the vast majority of people a steady and rewarding job can be of great benefit in reducing the risk of depression and engendering hap-piness. It is therefore not surprising that those recently made redundant, or who have been out of work for many months, are at a greater risk of developing depression than those in continuing employment.

Work, therefore, has a largely beneficial impact on mental health, but there are circumstances in which it can be less helpful. Although there is little evidence that poor working conditions can directly cause depres-sive illness, undue pressure and stress at work can combine with other problems, such as difficulties at home or recent unhappy events, and contribute to the development of depression.

Surveys have shown that certain kinds of work are linked to increased risks of job dissatisfaction and stress. Poor working conditions, such as cramped offices, noisy factories and hot and stuffy shops may all con-tribute to stress and tension.

Aspects of the work itself can be important. Jobs in which an employee feels there is little oppor-tunity to use his or her skills, or which are repetitive and inflexible seem particularly likely to result in job dissatisfaction and low morale. Uncertainty about how well a job is done, or about future changes in employment, can result in feelings of tension and worry. 'Difficult' bosses who bully and criticise will worsen any feeling of insecurity in their employees.

Employees who feel they have no say in the way their work is organised or that decisions are imposed from above will be prone to frustration. The introduction of new time-saving computer systems has beneficial effects on the efficiency of an office, but at the same time brings pressing deadlines and demands for quicker decisions, which may produce stress amongst employees. It has also had far-reaching consequences on the way businesses are structured, which can itself affect the people working within it.

So what can be done?

Every company should give consideration to the development of a 'mental health' policy. Such a policy would aim to provide a working environment which is conducive to the prevention of depression and other mental ill health, as well as its prompt and effective treatment. This would be expected to improve the overall performance of the organisation and of individual employees and to reduce costs incurred by sickness absence due to many physical illnesses in addition to those caused by depression.

There are four main areas where such a policy would concentrate:

1 Raising awareness
Everyone in the company, from the workforce to senior management, must be made aware of the importance of recognising and helping

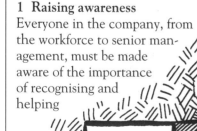

colleagues who may be suffering from depression. It is also fundamental that everyone understands that positive action can result in very great benefits to both individuals and the company as a whole.

2 Health education for employees
Employees will benefit from knowledge of mental health issues and instruction in specific techniques for reducing stress. Instruction in time management and assertiveness training, and the use of 'team-building' exercises may benefit all employees by protecting them from depression and other conditions. Identification of those employees needing assistance can be helped by educating the workforce and management with regard to early recognition of depression, and in what circumstances people become most vulnerable to developing depression. It is particularly important to emphasise the fact that depression is unlikely to permanently affect a person's ability to work.

3 The organisation of the business
The way in which a business is organised and operates is likely to have an effect on the mental health of its workforce. Important areas include the physical environment at work, the responsibilities inherent in the job and the level of supervision, and selection and training of

personnel for particular work. Thoughtful adjustments can enhance the job satisfaction of individual employees and the performance of the business as a whole.

4 Occupational health services
Occupational Health Departments need to be closely involved with senior management from the earliest stages in the development of programmes to educate line managers and the workforce in the prevention and early recognition of depression. They clearly also have a special role in the recognition, counselling and treatment of depressed employees and in facilitating their return to work. In particular, Occupational Health staff will have experience of sensitive issues such as workplace confidentiality, security of job tenure and the timing of the return to part or full-time working. They are also familiar with the particular stresses and strains of the work environment. Occupational Health nurses and doctors are well placed to work closely with family doctors or other specialist employees, whilst always bearing in mind the importance of issues of confidentiality in the workplace. Contacts should be established with the local branches of various self-help organisations.

The exact form of such a programme will of course depend upon the nature of the business as well as the size of the organisation. Any company can, however, expect to improve the management of their human resources in this way, with very great benefit to both the company and its employees.

From: *Defeat Depression*
A national campaign organised by the
Royal College of Psychiatrists
in association with the
Royal College of
General Practitioners

Community care

From the Mental Health Foundation

What is community care?

Community care is intended to provide help and support for people who could not otherwise manage on their own. The sort of people who may be eligible for community care include frail older, people, those with physical disabilities, drug or alcohol problems, learning disabilities or mental health problems.

Community care for people with mental health problems has been talked about ever since the early 1960s when it became widely accepted that the large, Victorian asylums were no longer appropriate and that care should be provided in the community where possible. There is now increasing concern that resources allocated for community care services do not match needs and that patients are sometimes being discharged from hospital without the necessary support being in place. The Mental Health Foundation has conducted a major Inquiry into Community Care of Severely Mentally Ill People to address some of the problems which have emerged. 'Creating Community Care', the report of the Inquiry, was published in September 1994.

Community care means that, where appropriate, services and support are provided in people's own homes or in a residential or care home rather than in hospitals. This is a Government initiative which began as a response to the many reports of inadequate treatment received by people. The policy is aimed at giving people as much independence as possible whilst continuing to care for and support them. It will prevent people becoming 'institutionalised' and enable them to develop relationships with friends and family.

Community care also considers the needs of carers, and aims to provide them with practical support and information.

Where does the money come from?

Funds for social and residential care in the community are transferred from Central Government and distributed to local authority social service departments. Each authority is then responsible for purchasing services from a wide range of providers.

Funds for health care in the community come from health authorities and Family Health Services Authorities who purchase services from hospitals, community mental health teams and GPs. There is not a direct connection between money saved from the closure of psychiatric hospitals and that allocated to community care.

Who is responsible for community care?

At present there are two routes to community care for people with mental health problems:

The local Social Services department has overall responsibility for co-ordinating social and residential care. This might mean making available such services as: home helps, district nurses, meals on wheels and day-care facilities.

Some services such as meals on wheels may not be provided free, but this varies according to individual local authority policies. Anyone can apply for help and the local authority should carry out an assessment of their needs but that does not necessarily imply an entitlement to services. It is the local authority's responsibility to decide who will receive services.

Each assessment should involve representatives from a number of the caring professions such as social workers, psychiatric nurses and doctors so that all medical and social needs can be considered. A carer or other friend or relative can attend the assessment and all findings must be put, in writing, to the user. An appeal is then possible if the user feels that a fair assessment has not be given.

If someone is assessed as needing social or residential care, a 'Care Manager' will be appointed to ensure

Q. Who cares for mentally ill people in the community?

Community based treatment and care

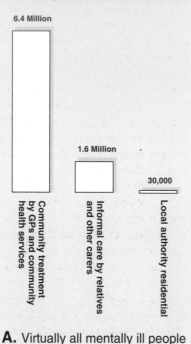

6.4 Million

1.6 Million

30,000

Community treatment by GPs and community health services

Informal care by relatives and other carers

Local authority residential

A. Virtually all mentally ill people in the community are treated by GPs and cared for by relatives.

that they get all the services they need.

If someone has been in hospital, even for a relatively short period of time, the most likely route to community care is via a process called the 'Care Programme Approach'. This is the responsibility of the local health authority. An individual after-care plan will be drawn up and the relevant service providers contacted before someone is discharged to ensure that full support is in place before they go home. A 'key worker' will be assigned to oversee the transition into living in the community and to liaise with service providers. It is a legal requirement for all patients admitted to hospital under the Mental Health Act 1983 to have a formal after-care programme prepared when they are discharged from hospital.

The two alternative routes to community care can cause confusion and uncertainty as to which agency has responsibility. This is an area to which our Inquiry paid particular attention.

What services are provided for carers?

If it has been mutually agreed that a friend or relative should act as a carer then assessments should consider the needs of the carer as well as the user. A carer has the right to receive all the practical support and information they need to continue to provide care. All social services departments are obliged to appoint an officer specifically to deal with complaints, and carers have the right to demand additional services if they feel they need them.

Is there still a need for psychiatric hospitals?

Community care does not mean that everyone will be able to cope in the community all the time. For a minority of severely mentally ill people who may be at risk to themselves or others, some form of hospital accommodation or sanctuary may be necessary from time to time in a crisis or for respite care. However, their base will remain in the community.

What about the particular needs of people who are seriously ill?

The Government has recently introduced some new measures in an attempt to ensure that people who may be at risk to themselves or others continue to receive support and supervision in the community. Health authorities are required to ensure that all hospitals and trusts providing mental health care set up 'supervision registers' which identify and provide information on those considered to be 'at risk'. Patients should normally be informed of this.

The Department of Health is also introducing a system of 'supervised discharge' under a new Mental Health Bill. This will mean that psychiatric patients who are discharged from hospital but considered at risk must comply with their treatment plan. If they do not, their case will be reviewed and they may be recalled into hospital.

© *Mental Health Foundation*
December, 1994

Q. Are psychiatric hospital populations declining?

Long-term Resident Patients – 1980s

Decline in long-stay population	Increase in 'new long-stay' population
	+ 15%
− 50%	

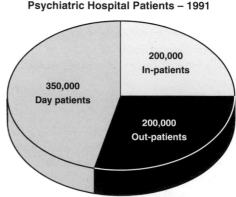

Psychiatric Hospital Patients – 1991

200,000 In-patients

350,000 Day patients

200,000 Out-patients

A. As total beds decline, long-stay patient numbers have halved. 'New long-stay' numbers have increased by 15%. More people occupy beds for shorter periods or make use of out-patient and day-patient services.

From: *Mental Illness: The Fundamental Facts* published by The Mental Health Foundation

Care that fails the mentally ill

By Vikki Orvice

Care in the Community isn't working, Government advisers admitted yesterday.

A severe shortage of emergency beds has led to sick patients being discharged from hospital to make way for others even more seriously ill.

In many cases there is little community support for them, and they pose a possible threat to the public.

The bleak picture of the official scheme for dealing with the mentally ill is revealed in a damning report by the Mental Health Task Force, which gives the first official evidence of the scale of the crisis.

It concentrates on London over the last six months, but highlights a nationwide problem and mirrors studies by the Royal College of Psychiatrists and mental health watchdogs. ✓

The report comes as doctors treating Tony Sarumi, the 24-year-old who threw himself into the lions' den at London Zoo earlier this month, claimed that they were forced to release him from hospital even though he still needed help.

Last year, following a similar incident involving schizophrenic Ben Silcock, the *Daily Mail* launched a campaign to improve community care for mental health patients.

Problems

The new study – compiled by 23 task force members including NHS executives, psychiatrists and social services experts – shows that Care in the Community is often non-existent and says more hospital beds are needed.

It calls for health authorities to consider slowing down the closure of Victorian asylums and to ensure that adequate support is available in the community before beds are closed.

The task force, while recognising many examples of good practice, said fundamental problems remained. It found evidence of poor communication with the mentally ill and an alarming ignorance of their needs.

Health authorities in many districts did not know how many mentally ill people they were responsible for.

Among other problems identified by the study – *Mental Health in London: Priorities for Action* – were a lack of supported housing for the homeless mentally ill and a 'significant need' to build up community-based services, including day centres.

The report says: 'Some patients with severe and chronic mental disorders are being discharged without adequate supervision and the provision necessary to meet their social and health needs.

'This could increase risk not only to public safety – but also to the safety of the staff in non-specialist accommodation or other services.'

The task force found evidence of 'major pressure' on beds in NHS medium-secure units. As a result, patients were being sent to private hospitals some distance away.

There were poor links between district health authorities, with GPs saying they felt isolated and found it difficult to get patients treated in emergencies.

David King, task force co-leader, said: 'It is vital that health and social services work together to ensure that an appropriate range of service is available. With good social support, the pressure on hospital beds will be reduced.'

Marjorie Wallace, of the mental health charity Sane, said: 'If those in charge had a more robust attitude, and greater access to psychiatric beds where there was skilled nursing care, the tragedies we hear about would not be happening.'

© Daily Mail
September, 1994

Photo: David Hoffman

In many cases there is little community support for sick patients being discharged from hospital to make way for others even more seriously ill

Eight community care myths

The following, by Liz Sayce, MIND's Policy Director, is an extract from MIND's community care campaign pack

Myth 1

'Closing psychiatric hospitals means people are being thrown out on to the streets.'

Facts

- Only 2 per cent of the people with clear mental health problems on London's streets have ever been long-stay psychiatric patients (two years or more).[1]
- Studies of people discharged from long-stay psychiatric hospitals show less than 2 per cent were 'lost' to follow-up by mental health services after a year. Some of these – but none of the other 98 per cent – may have become homeless.[2]

The scandal that many people in Britain are living on the streets, in bed and breakfast or in squats is caused mainly by the decline in affordable housing – not by the closure of psychiatric hospitals. The reason they are often mentally distressed is because being homeless is bad for your mental health; and because some people who already have mental health problems cannot get access to housing with the right sort of support.

The answer to this crisis is more housing, including housing with support. A hospital is no substitute for a home.

Myth 2

'We cannot sleep safely in our beds – our children are at risk.'

Facts

- A diagnosis of mental illness is not in itself a predictor of violence.[3]
- The factors that are associated with violence are being young and male (by age 31, one in 14 men born in 1960 had a conviction for violent crime);[4] and being under the influence of alcohol or drugs (studies show that in 66 per cent – 80 per cent of homicides, alcohol is involved).[5]
- Mentally disordered' offenders make up a tiny minority of all offenders. In 1991 only one in 600 of notifiable offences of violence against the person resulted in a court order for hospital treatment for mental disorder.[6]
- People diagnosed schizophrenic are 100 times more dangerous to themselves than to others.[7]
- Acts of violence committed by strangers are very rare: 85 per cent of attacks on women and 70 per cent of attacks on men are carried out by people they know.[4] We are all infinitely more at risk from our family and friends than from a mentally disturbed stranger.

A small number of people diagnosed mentally ill do pose a risk to the public when they are disturbed – during a 'psychotic episode' – sometimes with tragic results. They need to be in secure hospital provision. But the overwhelming majority of people diagnosed mentally ill are not violent. Despite this, a 1993 study found that two thirds of all media references to mental illness focused on violence.[8]

Users of mental health services are very distressed by their problems being constantly linked to danger in the public mind.

'I'm about as dangerous as a butterfly on valium' (service user).

The answer to this crisis is more housing, including housing with support

---

Myth 3

'All or most of the psychiatric hospitals have closed under the community care policy.'

Facts

- There are still 90 large psychiatric hospitals open in England, out of 130 open in the early 1960s, plus nine out of nine open in Wales.[9]
- The NHS still spends 77 per cent of its mental health budget on hospital and medication costs; and only 23 per cent on community mental health services such as community psychiatric nurses, day hospitals and counselling.[10]

The problem is not that all the hospitals have closed; the problem is that the money saved by beginning to run them down has often been spent on acute medicine or meeting NHS deficits – but not on community care.

Myth 4

'Community care is a new experiment – at least we knew hospital treatment worked.'

Facts

- It has been government policy to replace psychiatric hospitals with community services since the 1960s. Even before that community mental health services, like therapeutic communities, had been developed.
- In the 1990s there are countless examples of successful community care projects across Britain and across the world – for instance, those run by the 230 local MIND Associations.
- All available evidence – nationally and internationally – shows that properly funded community services work better than hospital care. A study of all comparisons between the two concluded 'no study found inpatient care to be better on any variable.'[11]

• Users of mental health services are highly dissatisfied with living in psychiatric institutions: they do not cure, but only contain; they are regimented and degrading; they are often not safe, with increasing reports of suicides by in-patients and of sexual and racial abuse of patients.

'It is impossible to feel you are anything but a small patient in a large machine.' (user contacting MIND). Although people need to know there is somewhere to go in times of crisis (a refuge or acute psychiatric unit) – and a few need a long-term secure hospital place – the vast majority of people diagnosed mentally ill, with the right support, can live successfully in the community most of the time.

Myth 5

'Community care might be OK if everyone took their medication.'

Facts

● Major tranquillizers (the treatment for people diagnosed schizophrenic) do not cure. They do not always ease the symptoms or prevent relapse: one study found 25 per cent of people taking them still relapsed within a year.[12]

● Some people find these drugs helpful, but they can also have serious adverse effects and risks. Professor Malcolm Lader of the Institute of Psychiatry estimates there is one death a week linked to major tranquillizers in Britain (often from unsafe dosages and/or dangerous combinations of drugs).

● There are alternatives, such as social support, cognitive therapy and self-help groups for people who hear voices. These approaches enable some people to take low dosages of drugs or do without them.

Myth 6

'People with mental health problems will never be accepted because they are different from everyone else – they even look different.'

Facts

● People with mental health problems look no different to anyone else – unless they are taking certain types of psychiatric drugs. Major tranquillizers can cause an irreversible disorder of the central nervous system called tardive dyskinesia, which makes people lose muscular control, particularly in the face. They may not be able to stop their tongue moving in and out of their mouth and they may grimace uncontrollably. Estimates of how many people on major tranquillizers experience this distressing disorder vary from 20 per cent to 72 per cent.[13]

● Studies of the general population show that 25 per cent of people experience some psychiatric symptoms – ranging from depression and anxiety to serious problems with thought or perception – each year.[14] Rabbi Lionel Blue, Joanna Lumley, Ludovic Kennedy and other well-known figures have openly talked about their own experiences of mental health problems.

People with mental health problems are not essentially different from others. Most of us at some point in our lives experience a mental health problem or know someone close to us who does.

Myth 7

'There is no such thing as 'community' – and it certainly doesn't care. So community care can't work.'

Facts

● People using mental health services are supporting each other through self-help groups and telephone networks – setting up their own 'communities' across the country. Some also get strong support from friends, relatives, local churches or mosques and other organizations.

● Surveys consistently show that the public supports the principle of community care – although they rightly believe it is not working well enough in practice as it is underfunded. A MIND/RSGB survey in 1994 found 72 per cent of the public supported community care; most would be prepared to pay a little more in tax to make it work.[15]

● Although some people resist community care developments in their own area (on the 'not-in-my-back-yard' principle), we are also seeing more examples of tolerant attitudes, both amongst the general public and those in positions of influence:
'There is no evidence to suggest that the conduct of the proposed occupiers, being people with problems of mental illness in the course of rehabilitation, would be more or less objectionable or anti-social than if the property were occupied, for example, as a boarding house for ten residents chosen at random from the community at large.'[16]

The public would become more tolerant still if they knew community care was properly funded; and if the Government passed legislation to outlaw unfair discrimination in employment and services against people with actual or perceived disabilities.

Myth 8

'Community care costs much more than hospital care – we'll never be able to afford it.'

Facts

● The cost of providing a community care service for a person discharged from a long-stay hospital is on average £493 per week – no more than providing a long-stay hospital bed.[17]

● Every individual is different and has different needs: for instance, one person may need daily help with practical tasks, another may need counselling for relationship difficulties, another may need to be in housing with 24-hour staff support. The old hospital system gave everyone roughly the same service, at the same cost, whatever their needs. A community care system can give each person a different service, at varying costs. Some people may need a more expensive service than the hospital; others will need a less expensive one. If everyone currently in psychiatric hospital who could benefit from community care was offered it, the average cost per person would not necessarily be higher. We do need a new injection of money – to make sure new services can be set up during (not after) the closure of the old hospitals; and to start providing a service for the millions who currently get little or nothing. But many people could get a better, more individual service, if we simply transferred existing money from hospitals to community care.

Reproduced from *OPENMIND* No 68, April/May 1994, the mental health magazine published by MIND and available on subscription from MIND. See page 39 for address details.

© *OPENMIND*
April/May, 1994

The community care campaign pack is available at £6 plus 10% p&p from MIND Mail Order, Granta House, 15–19 Broadway, Stratford, London E15 4BQ.

1 Team for the Assessment of Psychiatric Services (1990). *Better Out Than In?* North East Thames Regional Health Authority.
2 Craig T et al (1992). *Homelessness and Mental Health Initiative.* Second Report to the Mental Health Foundation. RDP.
3 Hamilton J R (1990). Dangerousness. *Psychiatric Bulletin.* Supplement 3. Abstracts.
4 *Social Trends* 1993. HMSO.
5 Gillies H (1976). Homicide in the West of Scotland. *British Journal of Psychiatry* 128. Virkkunen (1974). Alcohol as a Factor in Predicting Aggression and Conflict Behaviour Leading to Homicide. *British Journal of Addiction* 69.
6 *Home Office Statistics England and Wales.* 1990.
7 Prins H (1990). 'Dangerousness: A Review' in Bluglass R and Bowden P. *Principles and Practice of Forensic Psychiatry.* Longman.
8 Philo G et al (1993). *Mass Media Representations of Mental Health/Illness.* Report for Health Education Board for Scotland. Glasgow University Media Group.
9 Davidge M et al (1993). *Survey of English Mental Illness Hospitals.* Prepared for the Mental Health Task Force.
10 Mental Health Foundation (1993). *Mental Illness. The Fundamental Facts.* MHF.
11 Muijen M et al (1992). Home Based Care and Standard Hospital Care for Patients with Severe Mental Illness. *British Medical Journal* 304.
12 Leff J P and Wing J K (1971). Quoted in Lacey R (1991). *The Complete Guide to Psychiatric Drugs.* MIND/Ebury Press.
13 Bergen J A et al (1989). The Course of Tardive Dyskinesia in Patients on Long-term Neuroleptics. *British Journal of Psychiatry* 154.
14 Goldberg D and Huxley P (1980). *Mental Illness in the Community.* Tavistock.
15 MIND/Taylor Nelson Research Surveys of Great Britain (1994). *The Public's View of Mental Health Services.* MIND.
16 Lands Tribunal Judgement 12 January 1993.
17 Beecham J (1993). Funding Mental Health Services. *PSSRU Bulletin.* University of Kent.

Making community care work

Creating Community Care: Report of the Mental Health Foundation Inquiry into Community Care for People with Severe Mental Illness

There can be few initiatives which have caused as much controversy as the Government's Care in the Community policy. Is it a better response to the needs of severely mentally ill people than long stay psychiatric hospitals? Or is it failing those it is meant to be supporting?

Community care is intended to provide help and support for people who cannot otherwise manage on their own. Care for people with mental health problems has been talked about since the early 1960s, when it became generally accepted that the large Victorian asylums were no longer appropriate and that care should be provided in the community where possible.

In recent years there has been public anxiety over a number of highly publicised cases involving people with severe mental health problems who have not received the care they needed. In response, last September the charity, the Mental Health Foundation, set up an Inquiry: Community Care for People with Severe Mental Illness.

The overriding message from our Inquiry Report, *Creating Community Care*, published on 8 September 1994 is – community care can work if the right services are in place.

People with severe mental illness have similar needs to the rest of the population. They need an appropriate place to live, an adequate income, a social life, a job or other day activity, support, respect and trust. As well as meeting their needs, having these support services in place will also reassure the general public.

Additional resources for housing, health and social services such as residential care and home support are urgently needed. One immediate source of funding is the money saved from the closures of long stay hospitals.

Top of the Report's 38 recommendations is that the Prime Minister take action to improve community care provision for people who are severely mentally ill. Responsibility for co-ordinating and monitoring government departments involved in providing such care

Q. Where does the money go in caring for mentally ill people?

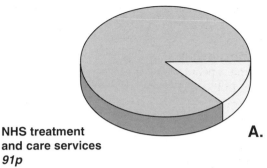

Local authority, private and voluntary care services
9p

NHS treatment and care services
91p

A. 91p in every £1 spent goes on NHS provision for mentally ill people. The remaining 9p goes on local authority, private and voluntary agency care in the community.

From: *Mental Illness: The Fundamental Facts*, published by The Mental Health Foundation

should be with a Cabinet Committee. These include the Department of Health, the Department of Environment, the Department of Social Security and the Home Office.

Current community care policy is fragmented and these departments often find themselves working against each other, rather than together.

The recommendations have been drawn up by many highly respected experts. They include Sir William Utting, former Chief Inspector at the Department of Health and Sir Peter Imbert, former Commissioner at the Metropolitan Police. The Report has been sent to the Prime Minister, Government Ministers, MPs, civil servants, Directors of Social Services and many others.

The Report also proposes there should be a national network of Community Mental Health Teams, jointly established by all health and local authorities. These consist of nurses, social workers, occupational therapists, psychologists and psychiatrists who are trained to work with people with a mental illness. The Teams should be the main providers of health and social care and the point of access for benefits advice, housing services and practical home support. All these services should include access to a 24 hour, 7 days a week crisis service for people with a severe mental illness.

Most people do not know what Community Mental Health Teams are, or what services they provide.

This must be changed. As increasing numbers of people move from hospitals which are closing, the public needs to be reassured that well known and well planned alternative services exist. Community Mental Health Teams should publicise their services locally and issue basic information such as names and addresses of key people to contact.

Severe mental illness affects an estimated 300,000 people. It could happen to any of us. It is not an issue the country can afford to ignore. We urge the Government to support our recommendations for improving the provision of care. We believe that if adopted, our recommendations would result in a real improvement in the quality of care and ensure that community care works. Everyone would then be reassured that services are in place for people with a severe mental illness.

Amongst the Inquiry's 38 recommendations are:

- that the Government should publish a single comprehensive statement setting out each agency/department's responsibilities;
- that the Department of Health should establish a standard system of managing care to end the present confusion;
- that every person with a severe mental illness should be assigned a Care Manager and Key Worker to ensure that proper care and support is provided;
- that the Government ensure that savings made from the closure of

long stay hospitals are reinvested into services in the community;
- that more resources are urgently required to manage the shortfall that exists between need and funding for housing, health and social care;
- that responsibility for planning, purchasing and delivery of services should be clarified, so that both organisations and individuals can be held accountable and responsible at every stage;
- that the Royal College of General Practitioners should review the procedures of care and degree of responsibilities of GPs towards people with a severe mental illness;
- that Family Health Services Authorities (FHSAs) should ensure that everyone, including people with a severe mental illness, is able to register with a GP.

If you want to find out what arrangements exist for people with severe mental illness in your area, write to the Chair of your Health Authority or the Chair of your Local Authority Social Services Committee and encourage them to publicise the availability of services.

• *Creating Community Care: Report of the Mental Health Foundation Inquiry into Community Care for People with Severe Mental Illness* is available from the Mental Health Foundation. Price £9.50.

© *The Mental Health Foundation*

Call for 24-hour crisis centres for the mentally ill

By David Fletcher, Health Services Correspondent

Crisis centres open 24 hours a day, seven days a week should be established in every area for mental health patients living in the community, the Mental Health Foundation recommends today.

It calls on the Government to ensure that every patient with severe mental illness should have a care manager to plan their care and a named key worker to ensure it is carried out.

They should be looked after by trained teams of nurses, social workers, psychiatrists and others who would ensure a point of contact was available at all hours to cope with crises.

The recommendations are made in a report by a committee – chaired by Sir William Utting, former chief inspector at the Department of Health – consisting of top specialists including Sir Peter Imbert, former Commissioner of the Metropolitan Police, and Viscountess Runciman, chairman-designate of the Mental Health Act Commission.

It follows widespread public concern over the care of psychiatric patients in the community prompted by the case of Ben Silcock, a schizophrenic who climbed into the lions' den at London Zoo, and reinforced by the death of Mr Jonathan Zito, stabbed at Finsbury Park Underground station by another psychiatric patient, Christopher Clunis.

The report was welcomed as 'constructive' by Mr John Bowis, junior health minister, who announced an extra £4.4 million for more places in secure settings.

It criticises the 'bewildering barrage of initiatives' set up for the care of psychiatric patients.

The report identifies three overlapping procedures for the care of the mentally ill – under the Mental Health Act, the Community Care Act and the Government's Care Programme Approach – and says they cause confusion and concern.

'Some services, particularly acute hospitals in inner cities, are under such pressure that proper discharge planning of any sort is an unattainable dream,' it says.

Some psychiatric hospitals are said to discharge patients into totally unsatisfactory after-care arrangements to make beds available for patients who might otherwise 'do something dangerous or drastic to themselves or others.'

The report estimates there are 300,000 people who need specialist mental health services every day – double the number of residents in large Victorian asylums when they reached their peak in 1954.

Closures of these old hospitals are estimated to have saved £2 billion but it is not clear where that has gone. The report says another £540 million a year is needed for mental health spending.

Mr David Blunkett, Shadow Health Secretary, said the report highlighted Government failure to protect those with severe mental illness and to offer protection to the public. 'We must have the 24-hour-a-day, seven-days-a-week crisis centres,' he said.

An inquiry was announced yesterday into how a schizophrenic who said he was a danger to the public was allowed to live in a hostel where he killed a care worker. John Rous, 48, was sent to Broadmoor in June.

Recommendations

The main points are:

- A Cabinet committee to co-ordinate and monitor departments giving community care.
- Standard system of managing care.
- Care manager and key worker assigned to every severely mentally ill patient.
- Savings from closure of long-stay mental hospitals reinvested in community services.
- Review of GPs' responsibilities towards severely mentally ill.
- Family Health Services Authorities to ensure everyone, including mentally ill, to register with a GP.
- More resources to close gap between need and funding for housing, health and social care.

New battle tactics

With the weight of public opposition stacked against them, opening mental health projects in the community is becoming a serious problem. The Mental After Care Association is working with a new softly, softly approach to help placate local concern, writes Sue Mapp

A new plan of campaign has been launched to stem the cry of 'Not in My Back Yard,' echoing down more and more streets as residents, ignorant and confused about people with mental health or learning difficulties, react fearfully and vocally to burgeoning plans to settle these clients in the community.

The Mental After Care Association (MACA) has drawn up pointers to ward off what, in its experience, is a 'bombardment' of opposition to proposals for housing even small groups of these clients.

Problems encountered by MACA will be all too familiar to other battle-weary voluntary and statutory agencies in this field. It has opened eight projects in the last nine months and experienced serious hostility to all bar one. MACA reports that the level of local concern has heightened recently – not least as a result of the media's sensational cataloguing of cases like that of Christopher Clunis, the diagnosed schizophrenic who killed an innocent bystander last year.

The lengths to which neighbours go to try and keep mental health projects out can be daunting. House deeds have been consulted to prove that buildings must be used solely as private dwellings or family homes. Equally alarming are the professionals – headmasters, doctors, solicitors, councillors, even social care staff – who object to such schemes, although a

National Schizophrenia Fellowship (NSF) scheme was saved by a supportive social worker living next door.

One of MACA's main recommendations is to keep each operation as low key as possible, bearing in mind that 'we're talking about a few people moving on to a street here,' says the charity's parliamentary and media officer Radhika Bynon.

MACA questions the legitimacy, and warns against the intrinsic dangers, of public meetings in these instances, and believes they should be avoided at all costs. The flowery language of opponents – words like 'secure unit,' 'inmates,' 'violence,' 'democracy' and 'accountability' – captures the headlines and results in the small group of clients moving in with a label and a fanfare. If a public

meeting has eventually to be held, MACA and NSF advise making it as informal as possible. Terry Hammond, NSF regional director, southern region, sometimes plants a willing diagnosed schizophrenic in the audience. When someone asks about the characteristics of future residents, he will say: 'David, would you like to tell this lady/gentleman how your illness affects you?'

To escape a public meeting, MACA suggests discussing information-sharing with neighbours at an early stage in its partnership with a local authority, health authority or NHS Trust.

It is possible to identify some opposition indicators, says MACA. These are:
- where there is a strong sense of community;
- where there are powerful residents' associations with outspoken leaders;
- where there has been organised protest of some type before; and
- where the project partner is poorly regarded in the area or there is much dissatisfaction with a local authority's services.

Letters (personalised if possible) to neighbours should give a named MACA contact and be supported with additional information about MACA. Approaches from the public should be addressed quickly, with an offer to meet individuals in their homes. Where neighbours are still unsatisfied, local councillors or other community leaders should be informed and their support enlisted.

If the number of opponents exceeds the scope of a private home, it may be worth considering a larger meeting for a closed group of people, such as the parents of a local school.

By restricting the meeting to a particular audience, it is easier to address specific concerns.

Open days are an effective means of introducing neighbours to staff and building positive relations, but these must be before users move in. 'We don't front the battle with users – we will fight it so they can get on and live their lives,' says Bynon.

The aim in all discussions with neighbours, advises MACA, is not to change people's long-held attitudes, but to address some of their real fears and ask them to be specific about them.

When the question of potential violence comes up, as it invariably does, MACA offers no guarantees, in the same way that none can be given about any member of the public. But it says the users have been assessed as suitable for community living.

Often neighbours worry about 'flashing', particularly where there are children, and MACA explains that, being anti-social behaviour, should it happen, it would be taken up with the user as it would be with anyone.

Neighbours also think users will 'stare,' 'look odd,' or wander the streets with nothing to do, so they need to be told about care plans. However it is strict policy, when asked who the residents will be, never to discuss individual cases.

Above all, it is important to stress the project planners' professionalism, says Bynon.

You have to convey: 'We know what we're doing here,' and reassure them that there is a project manager for them to refer to. The softly, softly touch is recommended by both MACA and NSF.

Hammond warns workers against banging tables and saying: 'These people have as much right to live here as you do, and they don't need to have your permission to do so.' This, of course, only serves to harden the opposition.

Neighbours also think users will 'stare,' 'look odd,' or wander the streets with nothing to do, so they need to be told about care plans

---

Nimby problem solved

A flagrant case of NIMBYism arose at Northover Court, Talbot Woods, Bournemouth, which had already received planning permission to house 20 elderly people. When it was offered instead to the National Schizophrenia Fellowship and Shaftesbury Housing Association, it was not deemed necessary to re-apply, as only the client group had changed.

Neighbours, who were afraid of the alternative clients, demanded, and considered they had a right to, more information.

The NSF, the housing association and Dorset social services agreed to meet them, choosing the comfortable surroundings of an old people's home as the venue. The press were not there.

Between 20 and 30 people attended and neighbours protested they had not been consulted.

They were mainly anxious about their children and the value of their houses falling.

They also said it was a dangerous road and inappropriate for people with mental health difficulties.

The project planners said they understood residents' concerns but did not agree with them and the meeting was reasonably polite apart from one verbally aggressive mother who said she would have to move.

The planners offered to show neighbours round other schemes but the offer was not taken up.

The neighbours then went to the press, which played a straight bat with the story, and the planners stood their ground.

Bournemouth Council, which had previously thrown out a similar NSF scheme, with a couple of councillors vehemently opposing it, had accepted a second since and on this third occasion, having seen one scheme in action, was very supportive.

There was further agitated correspondence in the press and it was rumoured that neighbours were trying to get an injunction to stop the scheme going ahead, but this did not materialise.

The scheme was established, the manager made himself known to neighbours, and after the clients had settled in, with their agreement a party was held to which neighbours were invited.

The atmosphere was warm; neighbours who had expressed initial fears said these had been allayed, and one woman made a point of saying how delighted she was with the scheme.

What objectors said about community projects

'Thirty-three murders in the past 18 months by people released from secure institutions – the 34th could be one of US! – Object now.'
(Mencap project, Great Yarmouth)

'The thought of your children having to pass this house is causing apprehension ... Families are uptight and there is a fear the kids would not get their freedom ...'
(Dundee Healthcare Trust project for people with learning difficulties)

'These patients should not be put right into the middle of a community like this. Maybe in a big house with its own grounds, not in a block of flats or a row of terraced houses. The public don't seem to realise they are getting good care in hospitals, and should still be in hospital until ... they are declared mentally fit.'
(Penumbra project, Mid Lothian)

'The patients may have a history of anti-social behaviour, or exhibitionism, or detention . . . Schoolchildren cannot be guaranteed protection from their unpredictable behaviour.'
(Penumbra project, East Lothian)

Does the community care?

Diverse provision for the mentally ill brings its own problems, argues Rosie Waterhouse

The caller said she was tired and had had enough. Her counsellor is away. She has to go to a day centre in three days' time, but last time she went there she didn't manage to tell them how bad she was feeling. She needed help now but she had nowhere to turn. She has started to plan how to die. She has stockpiled a cocktail of drugs. She has cried all morning but she is past tears now.

This is an account of a typical call last week from the daily log book kept by staff and volunteers at Saneline, a telephone helpline operated by the charity Sane, which offers information and advice to people suffering from all forms of mental illness, and their families. Set up in April 1992, the helpline answered 45,287 calls in the year up to July 1994. Another 92,002 people tried but failed to get through because all the lines were busy.

The calls to Saneline, which is London-based but launching a nationwide number next month, illustrate graphically the problems facing the increasing numbers of mentally ill people who are being cared for – or not – in the community.

Judging by an analysis of 417 calls to Saneline over three consecutive nights recently, the plight of mentally ill people and their families is desperate. More than half the calls concerned serious psychotic illness such as schizophrenia and manic depressive illness. Almost a quarter of calls were from people suffering from depression. Nearly half talked of the unmet need of the sufferer for medical treatment; nearly 40 per cent concerned a sufferer who was exhibiting violent, aggressive, bizarre or embarrassing social behaviour; one in five callers talked of suicidal feelings.

Sane estimates that one in four people suffer from mental illness at some time in their lives and one in seven have to seek medical treatment. The most common form of serious mental illness – and the one that most frequently makes headlines – is schizophrenia, a disorder which typically develops in late adolescence or early adulthood and affects an estimated 250,000 people in the United Kingdom.

Since the Sixties, successive governments have pursued the policy of closing the old mental asylums and treating more mentally ill people in the community, with care supposedly provided by a combination of health and social services. This week that policy came under renewed fire after a report published by the Royal College of Psychiatrists revealed there had been 34 killings in three years by patients who had been in contact with psychiatric services in the previous 12 months. The researchers blamed lack of coordination of support and failure by carers to interact.

The report led to calls for a halt to the hospital closure programme, and demands for more government money to build additional accommodation and employ extra doctors, nurses and social workers to care for this most vulnerable group.

So how have services for the mentally ill changed since the mental hospital closure programme began, and what is going wrong with care in the community?

The decision to close all 130 of the large mental institutions in England by 2000 was announced in 1961 by Enoch Powell, then Minister for Health, in an evocative speech conjuring up menacing images of the asylums which he said had to close. 'There they stand, isolated, majestic, imperious, brooded over by the giant water tower and chimney combined, rising unmistakable and daunting out of the countryside . . .'

By March 1993 only 38 of the institutions had closed, according to a Department of Health study carried out by researchers at Birmingham University's Health Services Management Centre. But they were some of the largest, and the number of beds has dropped from 140,000 in 1960 to 28,000.

However, the survey showed that the number of hospital beds and places in the community for mentally ill people has remained about the

same, falling from 92,234 in 1982 to 85,168 in 1992. The latest report, due next month from the Department of Health, shows a slight increase in total beds and places since last year.

What has changed dramatically is the mix of accommodation and level of supervision. The number of beds in the large mental hospitals has fallen from about 68,555 in 1982 to fewer than 28,448 in 1992. The number of psychiatric beds in district general and cottage hospitals has increased slightly from 15,145 to 21,830.

Local authority nursing homes appear to have increased their accommodation for the mentally ill from 4,173 beds in 1982 to 7,552 in 1992. However, the researchers are not sure whether the sharp rise in 1986 is because local authorities simply reclassified what used to be beds for the elderly as a new category, the elderly mentally infirm.

By far the biggest expansion has been in the voluntary and private sector. Voluntary residential places have risen from 1,603 in 1982 to 4,303 in 1992 and private places from 764 to 10,382. The number of private hospital beds is up from 1,994 to 12,653.

It is this change in the type of accommodation, and quality and quantity of care for the mentally ill – particularly the more serious cases – which most concerns mental health pressure groups. No national data is available on the level of care or amount of supervision in voluntary and private places. This can vary from bed-and-breakfast hotels and hostels, in which the patients fend for themselves, to private hospitals with 24-hour care, which was provided in the old mental institutions.

The National Schizophrenia Fellowship is calling for an extra £500m a year of government money to build new facilities and employ more staff. A report published by the group this week says that many acute urban psychiatric wards are operating at well above maximum occupancy levels and that at least another 350 medium-secure beds in regional units are needed to meet the Government's own targets.

Despite official figures that show beds and places remaining fairly static at about 85,000, the lack of accommodation has reached crisis point, according to the Institute of Psychiatrists. New guidelines for doctors on how to treat patients with schizophrenia, published this week, said: 'Accommodation, or the lack of it, is a source of anxiety to patients, carers and professionals alike. It underlies much of the breakdown in successful community care for people with schizophrenia and has contributed to some recent tragedies.'

The mental health charity Mind takes a significantly different stance from that of Sane. Mind puts first the rights of patients, and was one of the original campaigners in favour of caring for more people in the community. However, while supporting the principle of the hospital closure programme, Mind is also concerned that community care is not working in practice. It blames in part the professionals, for failing to follow guidelines on co-ordinating a 'care programme approach' for every discharged patient. Sane advocates far stricter controls on the seriously mentally ill who are a burden on their families or a danger. They believe more people need to be detained and treated in hospital. Mind objects to the Government's introduction of supervision registers – partly on civil liberties grounds. However, both would agree that better services in the community are needed.

Marjorie Wallace, a campaigning journalist who founded Sane, accuses the Government of turning the clock back 150 years. She argues: 'Community care can only work if services are available that actually replace those provided by a hospital, and if there is easy access to skilled medical care when a sufferer relapses and can no longer cope.'

'Many denied basic rights'

Millions of mentally ill people are still being denied fundamental rights – two years after the Government made mental health a priority, it was claimed yesterday.

The Mental Health Foundation claims action is urgently needed if sufferers of mental illness and people with learning disabilities are to live normal lives.

The call is made in the charity's annual report which sets out a 10 point plan setting out improvements.

Among the demands are:
- Government action to encourage employers to offer proper jobs to people with mental health problems;
- Views and needs of black people must be taken into account when services are planned;
- Daytime activities for people not in work;
- Advisory services on housing, benefits and legal matters to be available in all areas.

The report adds there must be more supported accommodation for people with learning disabilities.

June McKerrow, director of the Foundation, said, 'For far too long people with mental health problems and learning disabilities have been segregated from the rest of society, often in inappropriate living conditions.

'For there to be a real improvement in the quality of life for these people, the Mental Health Foundation is calling for urgent action to ensure that their needs and rights are met.'

Street level

**Dot Lott and Joe Pidgeon describe a
mental health team which has found new ways
to help homeless, mentally ill people**

Targeted and user friendly support services for homeless people with mental health problems are sorely lacking in many British cities. The problems of homeless people are increasingly in the public domain, and led the government to set up the Central London Homeless Mentally Ill Initiative in 1991.

The initiative had a number of objectives:

- to provide a flexible specialist community mental health and support advice service to staff of direct access agencies for single homeless people;
- to provide a case management service to single homeless people with mental health problems;
- to provide relevant training packages to staff in the voluntary and statutory sectors; and
- to improve access to health care, particularly mental health care for single homeless people.

The model adopted by Nottingham council in 1989 is a mental health support team located and managed in the voluntary sector, but integrated into health and social services networks. It has proven efficient and effective.

Consisting of three project workers and a team leader, the team worked with 253 'new' homeless clients last year – 158 requiring short, intensive work and 95 needing longer term support. A further 83 people were already on the books.

The circumstances of these clients reflect the downward spiral of events often associated with mental ill health, and the reality of homelessness which leads to deterioration in a person's mental health. There are few, if any, clients who have been discharged from long-stay psychiatric care.

Referrals to the team derive from three main sources: the 'surgeries' that the staff undertake in the evenings at all the homeless facilities; the weekly network meetings where the mental health support team community psychiatric nurse and district liaison nurse co-ordinate their work; individual referrals from GPs, the single homeless unit at the housing department, and mental health teams and hospitals.

Communicating essential information between hospital psychiatric teams and the support team has not proved problematic, and a high level of professional trust has developed in this partnership. Indeed, the support team is in effect acting as a screening service for GPs and psychiatric teams.

What is the key to the team's success? The city has a relatively well developed structure of community mental health services and alcohol and drugs services that pre-date the creation of the support team.

In addition, the early closure and transfer of long term psychiatric hospital services into the community has meant that a fairly diverse range of supported accommodation exists.

Single homeless people with mental health problems are often not well served by primary health care teams and GPs, and may not have contact with community mental health teams or alcohol and drugs services.

There are a number of reasons for this. GP practices are reluctant to register, and in many areas will only offer temporary registration or necessary emergency treatment, making access to psychiatric care virtually impossible.

On the consumer side, health care and remembering to keep appointments is a low priority to homeless people, already preoccupied about where they will sleep or when they will get their next meal. Life on the streets is a question of survival from minute to minute.

In this context, the support team offers a flexible and accessible service in the direct access hostels, in the homeless day services and on the

Photo: David Hoffman

The problems of homeless people are increasingly in the public domain

streets. They can provide the crucial link into health care agencies and community nursing that otherwise might never take place.

Another factor is the status of the workers who, clearly located within the voluntary sector's Hostels Liaison Group, don't carry with them what may be perceived as an 'official' or agency agenda.

Psychiatric nurse, doctor or social worker status may hinder the building of relationships, whereas the informal status of the team workers may facilitate contact and ongoing work with people who are homeless.

The majority of the direct access and homeless hostels are managed and run by the voluntary sector, and the team have a natural affinity and overlap with the work of hostel staff. Mutual understanding and trust facilitates good working relationships in this difficult area.

The profile of users helped by the team clearly illustrates the serious extent of mental distress and difficulty which may be on the margin of formal psychiatric diagnosis, and where, consequently, access to statutory services may be highly changeable.

User profiles

Mr S has displayed bizarre and disturbed behaviour since the age of 4. He was diagnosed as suffering from a 'personality disorder,' considered untreatable. The support worker built up a trusting relationship which enabled him to disclose past sexual abuse. This support continued over four years while Mr S was moved from one project to another due to unmanageable behaviour. The consistent support from one worker enabled him to recognise how he rejected projects before they could reject him, and he eventually remained in one project for a year. The team worker made contact with his family. Mr S is now living with them.

Ms Y is a young woman, who regularly inflicts self-harm and is a poly-drug user. The team arranged a psychiatric assessment then offered ongoing support and counselling over a previous rape. She moved into emergency accommodation and the team facilitated access to the drugs

This is a model of intervention that has much to recommend it if gaps in services for homeless, mentally ill people are to be more effectively plugged in our cities

and alcohol team and offered support.

Mr X had multiple problems, such as drug and alcohol abuse, and a history of violent offending. He received ongoing help from the support team to work through the underlying problems of grief over the break up of his marriage and on controlling his violence. The worker advocated access to his children and accompanied him to court over alcohol-related offences – subsequently helping him find more permanent accommodation and facilitating access to psychiatric services. Here it was discovered that he had suffered a brain trauma in the past which may have exacerbated the violent incidents.

Team history

Ten years ago people diagnosed with sociopathic personality disorder or challenging behaviour may have been admitted to psychiatric hospital if the circumstances warranted it. Changed thinking about what constitutes mental illness, the treatability clauses in the 1983 Mental Health Act, and the general decrease in bed space now mean that formal mental illness criteria invariably control admission.

The work of the mental health support team in the homelessness facilities therefore becomes more crucial for the carers and hostel staff

who are working every day with homeless people. Over the past five years the service has achieved a high level of credibility with all the main agencies involved in health care, social care and homelessness. This is reflected in the tripartite funding arrangements where the family health services authority, Nottinghamshire Social Service Department, and the Nottingham Health Care Trust all part-fund the service on a permanent basis.

The Department of Health has given it a 'model of good practice' designation and has invited the team leader to join the steering group for the Health Advisory Service's review on mental health and homelessness. And within the context of community care assessment the support team does complex assessments with its clients on behalf of the SSD. The team has become an effective model of intervention because it offers a quick response to a difficult, often unpopular, but needy client group. The team are conversant with the world of homelessness, its myriad problems and the frequent lack of responsiveness of homeless people to statutory service providers.

It is also aware of the needs of carers and hostel staff. In this regard they have delivered training on, among other things, coping with violence, mental health and homelessness, listening skills, personality disorder and alcoholism. Also, the team is strong in the support of homeless hostels and their staff, effectively linked into statutory and voluntary resources, and well targeted in terms of meeting needs at the point where homeless people most frequently fall out of service help.

This is a model of intervention that has much to recommend it if gaps in services for homeless, mentally ill people are to be more effectively plugged in our cities.

• By Dot Lott, leader of the mental health support team and Joe Pidgeon, service manager, health and disability, at Nottingham SSD.

© *Community Care*
October, 1994

Community care is working well says key report

Improved organisation rather than more money could help some mental patients cope better with life outside institutions, according to a key report on care in the community published today.

The Audit Commission inquiry into the country's mental health services said it was a 'popular perception' that Community Care was not working and posed a danger to both the public and patients.

The results were recently highlighted by the tragic death of Mr Jonathan Zito – a complete stranger fatally stabbed by diagnosed schizophrenic Christopher Clunis – and the cases of Mr Ben Silcock and Mr Tony Sarumi who both climbed into the lion's den at London Zoo.

But the Commission said that closing large institutions for the mentally ill was not responsible for the rising number of people on the street.

'Very few of them have spent more than a year in hospital, thus refuting the notion that large numbers of homeless and visibly mentally ill people have simply been

> *The problem is one of targeting money, rather than a shortage of funds*

"tipped out" on to the streets,' the report said.

It said there were some psychiatric patients among the homeless but most are not dangerous and were more likely to be quiet and withdrawn faced with the demands of everyday life.

Audit Commission controller Mr Andrew Foster said: 'The problem is one of targeting money, rather than a shortage of funds.

'We have found overqualified staff being used to carry out the sort of practical care that could easily be done by auxiliary staff for much less money.'

However, Ms Eve Thompson, of the National Schizophrenic Fellowship, said that while it welcomed the report it was concerned that it may be used to speed up hospital closures leading to more poorly planned and

unco-ordinated services and greater chaos in the community

'The Government continually introduces new guidance and new systems with no new resources behind them; we did not expect the Audit Commission to repeat this rhetoric,' she said.

But the report said comprehensive locally-based care had yet to be fully tried and too much of the available budget was still spent on hospitals. Two thirds of the £1.8 billion spent each year is tied up providing in-patient beds in hospitals costing over £600 per week, it stressed.

Instead hospital and community health should function as one, sharing common criteria for providing services.

Run-down inner cities needed more mental health care but the way money was allocated did not match demand, it said. Some inner-city neighbourhoods spent less than average while more affluent areas may spend twice as much on less acute needs.

© *Birmingham Post*
October 1994

INDEX

ADDITIONAL RESOURCES

You might like to contact the following organisations for further information. Due to the increasing cost of postage, many organisations cannot respond to inquiries unless they receive a stamped, addressed envelope.

Alzheimers Disease Society
158 Balham High Road
London SW12 9BN
Tel: 01781 675 6557

AMNASS (Amnesia Association)
7 King Edward Court
King Edward Street
Nottingham NG1 1EW
Tel: 01602 240800

Arbours Association
6 Church Lane
London N8 7BU
Tel: 0181 340 7646

British Association for Social Psychiatry
c/o Dept of Mental Health Sciences
St George's Hospital Medical School
London SW17 0RE

British Association of Psychotherapists
121 Hendon Lane
London N3 3PR

Childline
2nd Floor, Royal Mail Building
Studd Street
London N1 0QW
Tel: 0171 239 1000

Children's Legal Centre
20 Crompton Terrace
London N1 2UN
Tel: 0171 359 9392

Depressives Associated
PO Box 1022
London SE1 7QB
Tel: 01781 760 0544

Ex-Services Mental Welfare Society
Broadway House
The Broadway
London SW19 1RL
Tel: 0181 543 6333

Hamlet Trust
79 Clifton Road
London W9 1SZ
Tel: 0171 499 8677

Mental Health Foundation
37 Mortimer Street
London W1N 7RJ
Tel: 0171 580 0145

Mental Health Media Council
380-384 Harrow Road
London W9 2HU
Tel: 0171 286 2346

Mental Health Review Tribunals Offices
Block 1, Spur 5
Canons Park,
Government Buildings
Stanmore
Middlesex HA7 1AY
Tel: 01602 410304

MIND
Granta House
15-19 Broadway
London E15 4BQ
Tel: 0181 519 2122

National Society for the Prevention of Cruelty to Children (NSPCC)
National Centre
42 Curtain Road
London EC2A 3NH
Tel: 0171 825 2500

NCH Action for Children
85 Highbury Park
London N5 1UD
Tel: 0171 226 2033

NEWPIN
Sutherland House
35 Sutherland Square
London SE17 3EE
Tel: 0171 703 6326

Northern Ireland Association for Mental Health
Beacon House
80 University Street
Belfast BT7 1HE
Tel: 01232 328474

NSF (National Schizophrenia Fellowship)
28 Castle Street
Kingston-Upon-Thames
Surrey KT1 1SS
Tel: 0181 547 3937

Parentline
Westbury House
57 Hart Road
Essex SS7 3PD
Tel: 01702 554782

Resource Network for Adolescents
DLI
Mill Lane
Alderley Edge
Cheshire SK9 7UD
Tel: 01565 873929

Royal College of Psychiatrists
17 Belgrave Square
London SW1X 8PG
Tel: 0171 235 2351

SANE
2nd Floor
199–205 Old Marylebone Road
London NW1 5QP
Tel: 0171 724 8000 (London)
Tel: 0345 678000 (outside London)

Schizophrenia Association of Great Britain
International Schizophrenia Centre
Bryn Hyfryd
Bangor
Gwynedd LL57 2AG
Tel: 01248 354048

The Children's Society
Edward Rudolf House
Margery Street
London WC1X 0JL
Tel: 0171 837 4299

The Samaritans
10 The Grove
Slough SL1 1QP
Tel: 01753 532713

ACKNOWLEDGEMENTS

The publisher is grateful for permission to reproduce the following material

Chapter One: Mental Health

Emotional and mental health problems in the young, © The Mental Health Foundation, January 1995, *Mental illness among children up to 25% in 5 years*, © The Independent, 23rd May 1994, *Surviving adolescence*, © Royal College of Psychiatrists, April 1993, *Why do young minds matter?*, © Young Minds, The National Association for Child and Family Mental Health, *Mental illness*, © HMSO Reproduced with the kind permission of Her Majesty's Stationery Office, February 1995, *Mental health on the streets*, © The Big Issue, 6-12 February 1995, *Met rethink on mentally ill*, © Time Out Magazine, 18-25 January 1995, *Antidepressants: your questions answered*, © MIND, March 1994, *One in seven adults hit by mental disorder*, © The Independent, 15th December 1994, *Three experiences of madness*, © Sane, Summer, 1994, *Time to jettison the Mental Health Act*, © The Independent, 18th January 1995 page 18, *Suicide factsheet*, © MIND, January 1995, *Mental health and older people*, © The Mental Health Foundation, November 1994, *Depression in the workplace*, © Defeat Depression/ Royal College of Psychiatrists/ Royal College of General Practitioners.

Chapter Two: Community Care

Community care, © The Mental Health Foundation, December 1994, *Care that fails the mentally ill*, © Daily Mail, 28th September 1994 page 15, *Eight community care myths*, © MIND, April/May 1994, *Making community care work*, © The Mental Health Foundation, February 1995, *Call for 24-hour crisis centres for the mentally ill*, © The Telegraph Plc, London 1994, *New battle tactics*, © Community Care, 22-28 September, 1994 page 22-23, *Does the community care?*, © The Independent, 19th August 1994, *'Many denied basic rights'*, © Western Mail, 28th September 1994, *Street level*, © Community Care, 6-12 October, 1994 page 26-27, page 24-25, *Community care is working well says key report*, © The Birmingham Post, October, 1994.

Photographs and illustrations

Pages 1, 12, 22, 33: A. Smith / Folio Collective, pages 10, 31, 37: Ken Pyne, pages 11, 27: A. Haythornthwaite / Folio Collective, page 13: SANE, pages 15, 18, 20, 21, 24, 29: The Mental Health Foundation, pages 16, 19, 25, 35: David Hoffman, pages 23, 30: K. Fleming / Folio Collective.

Craig Donnellan
Cambridge
May, 1995